BASIC PHYSICS
(for Engineering Students)

BASIC PHYSICS
(for Engineering Students)

Binayak Dutta-Roy
Debajyoti Dutta-Roy

NEW AGE
WBUT

An Imprint of

NEW AGE INTERNATIONAL (P) LIMITED, PUBLISHERS

New Delhi • Bangalore • Chennai • Cochin • Guwahati • Hyderabad
Jalandhar • Kolkata • Lucknow • Mumbai • Ranchi
Visit us at www.newagepublishers.com

Branches:

- No. 37/10, 8th Cross (Near Hanuman Temple), Azad Nagar, Chamrajpet, **Bangalore**-560 018. Tel.: (080) 26756823, Telefax: 26756820, E-mail: bangalore@newagepublishers.com
- 26, Damodaran Street, T. Nagar, **Chennai**-600 017. Tel.: (044) 24353401, Telefax: 24351463 E-mail: chennai@newagepublishers.com
- CC-39/1016, Carrier Station Road, Ernakulam South, **Cochin**-682 016. Tel.: (0484) 2377004, Telefax: 4051303. E-mail: cochin@newagepublishers.com
- Hemsen Complex, Mohd. Shah Road, Paltan Bazar, Near Starline Hotel, **Guwahati**-781 008. Tel.: (0361) 2513881. Telefax: 2543669, E-mail: guwahati@newagepublishers.com
- No. 105, 1st Floor, Madhiray Kaveri Tower, 3-2-19, Azam Jahi Road, Nimboliadda, **Hyderabad**-500 027. Tel.: (040) 24652456, Telefax: 24652457, E-mail:hyderabad@newagepublishers.com
- RDB Chambers (Formerly Lotus Cinema)106A, 1st Floor, S.N. Banerjee Road, **Kolkata**-700 014. Tel.: (033) 22273773, Telefax: 22275247, E-mail:kolkata@newagepublishers.com
- 16-A, Jopling Road, **Lucknow**-226 001. Tel.: (0522) 2209578, 4045297, Telefax: 2204098 E-mail: lucknow@newagepublishers.com
- 142C, Victor House, Ground Floor, N.M. Joshi Marg, Lower Parel, **Mumbai**-400 013. Tel.: (022) 24927869. Telefax: 24915415, E-mail: mumbai@newagepublishers.com
- 22, Golden House, Daryaganj, **New Delhi**-110 002. Tel.: (011) 23262370, 23262368, Telefax: 43551305. E-mail: sales@newagepublishers.com

ISBN : 978-81-224-3067-7

Rs.125.00

C-10-04-4485

Printed in India at Mohanlal Printers, Delhi.
Typeset at Aakriti Graphics, Delhi.

PUBLISHING FOR ONE WORLD
NEW AGE INTERNATIONAL (P) LIMITED, PUBLISHERS
4835/24, Ansari Road, Daryaganj, New Delhi-110002
Visit us at **www.newagepublishers.com**

Preface

"Basic Physics (for Engineering Students)" is a textbook for the compulsory course (First Year First Semester) in Physics for all B.E./B.Tech. students as taught in various colleges in India. For concreteness we have used the syllabus (which has evolved through practice over several years) in the colleges under the West Bengal University of Technology. It is valuable for engineering and technology students of other universities as well.

Accordingly, we have divided the course material into three modules. Each module is logically divided into chapters and each chapter sub-divided into sections.

Module 1 deals with Classical Mechanics, from Newtonian Mechanics to the Hamiltonian Formalism. Several solved problems in this and the succeeding portions of the book are provided to clarify the underlying concepts and methods.

Module 2 deals with Vibration and Waves and illustrative examples are used to clarify the basic ideas.

Module 3 (Electricity and Magnetism) meticulously deals with specific problems, building up from the fundamentals of Electrostatics to the Maxwell's Equations and Electromagnetic Waves.

In order to make the book self-contained, all necessary mathematical tools have been developed in a simplified manner.

Together with a companion volume on Modern Physics, which is under preparation and a book of questions and solved examples to be published soon we intend to provide a user-friendly introduction to the background of physics needed by students of engineering and technology in India.

New Age International Pvt. Ltd. deserves praise for their painstaking efforts in putting into form the final shape of this book.

Binayak Dutta-Roy
Debajyoti Dutta-Roy

West Bengal University of Technology

SYLLABUS OF ENGINEERING PHYSICS COURSE

First Year B.E./B.Tech.
(ME, CE, BT, FT, CHE, PE, IT, CSE, BME, Marine, LT, TT, Ceramic, AUE)
from 2007

Code: PH-101
Contacts: 4L
Credits: 4

Module 1: Classical Mechanics

1.1 Newtonian Mechanics – Newton's laws of motion-system of particles (2 body problem) conservation of linear and angular momentum (1D and 2D elastic and in-elastic collision) and related problems.

4L

1.2 Lagrangian formulation – difficulties to handle coupled equations, Constraints (both time dependent and time independent), Degrees of freedom, Generalised co-ordinates, Generalised force, potential and kinetic energy, Lagrange's equation of motion and Lagrangian, Ignorable co-ordinates, Hamilton's equation and Hamiltonian. The course should be discussed along with physical problems of 1-D motion).

6L

Module 2: Vibrations and Waves

Simple harmonic motion – its expression and differential equation and solution, Superposition of two linear SHMs (with same frequency), Lissajous' figures.

Damped vibration – differential equation and its solution, Critical damping, Logrithmic decrement, Analogy with electric circuits. Forced vibration – differential equation and solution, Amplitude and Velocity resonance, Sharpness of resonance and Quality factor, Progressive wave equation of its differential form, Difference between elastic (mechanical), and electromagnetic waves.   8L

Module 3: Electricity and Magnetism

3.1 Examples of vector and scalar, field, grad, div, curl, Line integral, surface integral, volume integral, physical examples in the context of electricity and magnetism, Stokes theorem and Gauss theorem [No Proof], Expression of grad, div, curl and Laplacian in Spherical and Cylindrical co-ordinates.   6L

3.2 Coulomb's law, Gauss's law in integral form and conversion to differential form and application,

Coulomb's theorem, Electrostatic potential and field, Poisson's eqn. and Laplace's eqn. (Application to Cartesian, Spherically and Cylindrically symmetric systems – effective 1D problems) Electric current, drift velocity, current density, continuity equation, steady current, conservation of charge, ampere, esu. 7L

3.3 Lorentz force, force on a small current element placed in a magnetic field, Biot-Savart law and its simple applications, divergence of magnetic field, vector potential, Ampere's law in integral form and conversion to differential form – applications. 5L

3.4 Faraday's law of electo-magnetic induction in integral form and conversion to differential form, Maxwell's field equations, Concept of displacement current, Maxwell's wave equation and its solution for free space. 4L

Total Number of Lectures = 40

Contents

Module One : Classical Mechanics

MODULE TWO : VIBRATIONS AND WAVES

MODULE THREE : ELECTRICITY AND MAGNETISM

Module One

CLASSICAL MECHANICS

1 — Basics of Newtonian Mechanics

Newton's Laws of Motion are easily stated:

First Law: Every 'body' continues in a state of rest or uniform motion in a straight line unless compelled to change that state by forces impressed upon it.

Second Law: The rate of change of momentum of a particle is proportional to the impressed force and occurs in the direction in which the force acts.

Third Law: To every action there is always opposed an equal and opposite reaction.

Yet each of these laws contain concepts and underlying assumptions that need to be clearly understood.

Thus, the first law asserts that we can conceive of a frame of reference in which a body would be totally free of any interaction whatsoever. Assuming that all interactions fall off with distance this could be imagined to be a frame far away from all matter in the universe and at rest with respect to that. This or any other frame in uniform motion in a straight line (rectilinear) with respect to that will constitute the so-called **inertial frame of reference**. It is in such inertial frames that the laws of motion to follow are to be stated. Implicitly we have also assumed that space is described as per the appropriate three dimensional generalization of Euclid's elements of geometry defined in a plane [this is known as **Euclidean Space**] and also the notion that **time flows uniformly** and relentlessly in which things happens (viz. time is absolute regardless of where we are and what is happening). Also the use of the word 'body' needs amplification particularly with regard to its 'position' at a given time t and its 'state of motion'. In this context it is preferable to start with a more primitive concept viz. that of a **particle** — a quantity of matter abstracted to be a point and thus in one dimension would at a time t occupy the position $x(t)$ and in three dimension $\vec{r}(t) = x(t)\hat{i} + y(t)\hat{j} + z(t)\hat{k}$ with respect to the chosen inertial frame of reference. To specify the state of motion at a given time we need the notion of the **instantaneous velocity** to define which Newton invented Differential Calculus. The rate of change with time of the position of a particle (say in one dimension to begin with) is defined to be the limit

$$\underset{\Delta t \to 0}{Lt} \frac{x(t + \Delta t) - x(t)}{\Delta t} = \frac{dx(t)}{dt} = v(t)$$

and similarly the rate of change of velocity viz. the instantaneous acceleration is

$$\underset{\Delta t \to 0}{Lt} \frac{v(t + \Delta t) - v(t)}{\Delta t} = \frac{dv(t)}{dt} = \frac{d^2}{dt^2} x(t)$$

A measure of the quantity of matter in the particle will also need to be indicated and this is what we shall call the **mass of the particle** and denote it by m.

Thus the first law states that a particle of mass m in an inertial frame of reference will be either in a state of rest $\vec{v}(t) = 0$ for all time or with velocity $\vec{v}(t) = \vec{u}$ (a constant time independent vector) that is in a fixed direction pointing along $\vec{u}$ and of fixed magnitude (uniform rectilinear motion).

It may also be emphasised that in practice we only have **approximately** inertial frames in the laboratory for instance if we do carefully designed experiments such as those involving the Foucault's Pendulum we can see that the laboratory together with the earth is actually rotating. But over shorter time scales our laboratory table with balanced forces and frictionless (or rather reduced friction) surfaces provide us with nearly inertial frames of reference.

The second law goes on to state that this state of rest or uniform rectilinear motion in an inertial frame of an isolated particle of mass m and moving, let us say, with a velocity $\vec{v}$, can be changed only through an external agency providing a **force** which has a **magnitude** and a **direction** and hence is a vector $\vec{F}$, and that the rate of change of **momentum** (defined as $\vec{p} = m\vec{v}$) with time is proportional to the cause of this change, namely, the force. The rate of change of momentum with time at any instant is $\frac{d}{dt}(\vec{p}) = \frac{d}{dt}(m\vec{v})$ and this must be according to the law proportional to the force $\vec{F}$ responsible for this change. Units are always so chosen that the constant of proportionality is unity so that

$$\frac{d}{dt}(\vec{p}) = \frac{d}{dt}(m\vec{v}) = \vec{F} \qquad \qquad ...(1)$$

This is known as the **Newton's Equation of Motion**. For example, in the centimetre, gram, second or CGS system of units where the units of length is a centimetre, that of mass is a gram and of time is the second, the unit of force is a dyne. A dyne is a force which when acting on a particle of mass one gram causes an acceleration of 1cm/sec^2. Note that $\frac{d\vec{p}}{dt} = m\frac{d\vec{v}}{dt} = m\frac{d^2\vec{r}}{dt^2}$ viz. mass into acceleration (or rate of change of velocity). Where $\vec{r}$ defines the position vector of the particle.

Similarly in the MKS (or metre, kilogram, second) system the unit of force is taken to be a Newton which is that force which when acting on a kilogram mass would cause it to accelerate at the rate of 1metre/sec^2. Here at the basic level we have quite properly taken the mass to be time independent. However in applications which we may consider later such as a falling rain-drop from which water may be evaporating as it falls or the motion of a rocket which continually loses mass as a consequence of the ejection of the jet of gases, the equation of motion is best written in the form that we have adopted $\frac{d\vec{p}}{dt} = \frac{d\,m\vec{v}}{dt} = \frac{d\,m}{dt}\vec{v} + m\frac{d\vec{v}}{dt} = \vec{F}$, retaining the extra term $\frac{dm}{dt}$ due to the mass change.

A further matter to be emphasised is that though we begin from the conceptually simple system of a point particle we may extend the basic ideas to the motion of a system of particles. A rigid body may be treated as a special kind of multiparticle system in which the relative distances between the particles are fixed. Furthermore one may take a continuous limit of a many particle system and study the mechanics of continuous media; elastic solids and fluids.

The meanings of the words action and reaction in the context of the third law is that if two bodies are in isolation and constitute a closed system then the force of particle 2 on particle 1 viz. $\vec{F}_{1\Rightarrow2}$ is equal in magnitude but opposite in sign to that of particle 1 on particle 2 viz. $\vec{F}_{2\Leftarrow1}$, namely $\vec{F}_{1\Leftarrow2} = -\vec{F}_{2\Leftarrow1}$ and that these forces act along the line joining them. Thus for instance in the case of the gravitational force between two particles of masses m_1 and m_2 located at the points $\vec{r}_1$ and $\vec{r}_2$

$$\vec{F}_{1\Leftarrow2} = -Gm_1m_2 \frac{\vec{r}_1 - \vec{r}_2}{|\vec{r}_1 - \vec{r}_2|^3}$$

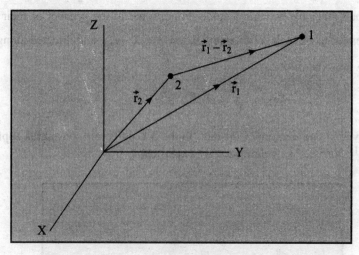

Fig. 1

where G is the universal constant of gravitation.

An extremely important consequence of this law is the **conservation** of **total momentum**. This is something borne out to be correct on the basis of all experiments done so far. To see how this follows from the third law consider an isolated system of two particles 1 and 2. From the second law and Newton's equations of motion for the rate of change of the momenta of particles 1 and 2, we have

$$\frac{d}{dt}\vec{p}_1 = \vec{F}_{1\Leftarrow2} \qquad\qquad\qquad ...(2a)$$

$$\frac{d}{dt}\vec{p}_2 = \vec{F}_{2\Leftarrow1} \qquad\qquad\qquad ...(2b)$$

adding which we get

$$\frac{d}{dt}(\vec{p}_1 + \vec{p}_2) = \vec{F}_{1\Leftarrow2} + \vec{F}_{2\Leftarrow1} = 0 \qquad\qquad ...(2c)$$

the last step being a consequence of the third law.

Thus the total momentum of these two particles $\vec{p}_1 + \vec{p}_2$ is time independent and hence remains constant or is conserved.

Section 2. GRAVITATION DUE TO EXTENDED BODIES

Since Newton created his mechanics and law of gravitation by considering two body problems: the proverbial apple accelerating as it falls towards the earth, the motion of the earth and other planets around the sun (obeying the Kepler's Laws) and that of the moon around the earth, it is only proper that we begin by laying down the basics of such two body problems.

Starting with point particles and stating the Laws of Motion in that context Newton began by assuming that the force of gravitation between two particles located at $\vec{r}_1$ and $\vec{r}_2$ with masses m_1 and m_2 would attract each other by exerting a force proportional to the product of their masses, with an inverse square dependence on their relative separation $r = |\vec{r}_1 - \vec{r}_2|$ and directed along the line joining them viz. along the unit vector $\hat{r} = \vec{r}/r$

$$\vec{F} = -\frac{Gm_1m_2\hat{r}}{r^2} \qquad \qquad ...(3)$$

where G is the Universal Gravitational Constant. In the S.I. units this constant is approximately given by $G = 6.67 \times 10^{-11}$ Nm²/kg² as determined by experiment.

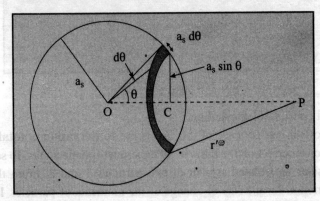

Fig. 2a Field at P due to uniform shell of radius a_s ($OP = r$, $OC = a_s \cos \theta$, $CP = r - a_s \cos \theta$)

It is however important to calculate the gravitational force exerted on a particle by a distribution of mass. We begin by finding the gravitational force on a particle of unit mass due to a spherical shell of uniform mass density per unit area and use that result to determine the result for a spherical body of spherically symmetric mass distribution which can be looked upon as a sum of concentric spherical shells. Consider a thin homogeneous spherical shell of radius as with mass density σ per unit area. This shell then has a mass of $M_s = 4\pi a_s^2 \sigma$. We wish to calculated the gravitational force due to this shell with its centre located at O on a unit mass placed at a point P outside the sphere and at a distance $OP = r$ from the centre of the shell, as shown in Fig. 2a above. We divide the shell into rings with centre C on the line OP as depicted in the diagram having radius $a_s \sin\theta$ circumference $2\pi a_s \sin\theta$ and with a width $a_s\, d\theta$ and hence of area $2\pi a_s^2 \sin\theta\, d\theta$ and mass $\sigma a_s^2 \sin\theta\, d\theta$.

Focussing on the ring shown above (the shaded region) and detailed below, we calculate the force on the unit mass placed at P due to the ring. We note that all elements on this ring are at the same distance, namely, $\sqrt{(AC)^2 + (CP)^2} = r' = \sqrt{(a_s \sin\theta)^2 + (r - a_s \cos\theta)^2} = \sqrt{a_s^2 + r^2 - 2a_s r \cos\theta}$ from P. Note that for every element on the ring (say the one shown in Fig. 2b by the shaded area at A) there is

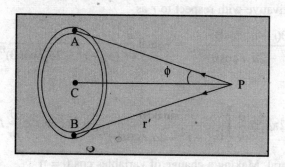

Fig. 2b Field at P due to the ring

a diametrically opposite element (shown by the shaded element at B) exerting attractive gravitational forces of equal magnitude (as the distance $AP = BP$ and the elements have the same mass) but directed along PA and PB respectively. One immediately realizes that the components of these forces perpendicular to the line PC (namely that joining the point P also to the centre O of the spherical shell), being equal and opposite, exactly cancel each other. The only surviving component of the force is that directed towards the centre which is the magnitude of the force multiplied by $\cos\phi$.

$$\vec{F}_{\text{Ring}} = -\hat{r} \cdot \frac{G \cdot 1 \cdot 2\pi a_s^2 \sigma d\theta}{(a_s^2 + r^2 - 2a_s r \cos\theta)} \cdot \cos\phi$$

the denominator being the square of the distance of each point on the ring from P, the numerator being the product of the masses at P (which is 1) and the ring multiplied by the Universal Gravitational Constant G, $\cos\phi$ giving the contributing component and $-\hat{r}$ indicating the direction of the net force. As can be seen from Fig. 2b we have

$$\cos\phi = \frac{CP}{BP} = \frac{r - a_s \cos\theta}{r'} = \frac{r - a_s \cos\theta}{\sqrt{a_s^2 + r^2 - 2a_s r \cos\theta}}$$

which when inserted into the expression for $\vec{F}_{\text{Ring}}$ gives

$$\vec{F}_{\text{Ring}} = -\hat{r}\, G\, 2\pi a_s^2 \sigma \frac{\sin\theta (r - a_s \cos\theta)\, d\theta}{(a_s^2 + r^2 - 2a_s r \cos\theta)^{3/2}}.$$

Since the spherical shell can be divided into such co-axial rings each giving a force at P in the same direction (towards the centre) and with θ ranging from 0 to π, we may obtain the force due to the spherical shell by integrating over θ to get

$$\vec{F}_{\text{Shell}} = -\hat{r}\, G\, 2\pi a_s^2 \sigma \int_0^\pi \frac{\sin\theta (r - a_s \cos\theta)}{(a_s^2 + r^2 - 2a_s r \cos\theta)^{3/2}}\, d\theta$$

Though the integral looks formidable at first sight one may note that the integrand may be written in as a partial derivative with respect to r as

$$\frac{\sin\theta (r - a_s \cos\theta)}{(a_s^2 + r^2 - 2a_s r \cos\theta)^{3/2}} = -\sin\theta \frac{\partial}{\partial r} \frac{1}{(a_s^2 + r^2 - 2a_s r \cos\theta)^{1/2}}$$

and hence

$$\vec{F}_{\text{Shell}} = \hat{r}\, G\, 2\pi a_s^2 \sigma \frac{\partial}{\partial r} \int_0^\pi \frac{\sin\theta\, d\theta}{(a_s^2 + r^2 - 2a_s r \cos\theta)^{1/2}} = \hat{r}\, G\, 2\pi a_s^2 \sigma \frac{\partial}{\partial r} I(a_s, r)$$

where $I(a_s, r)$ is the integral. Making a change of variables $\cos\theta = \eta$ we obtain

$$I(a_s, r) = \int_0^\pi \frac{\sin\theta\, d\theta}{(a_s^2 + r^2 - 2a_s r \cos\theta)^{1/2}} = \int_{-1}^{+1} \frac{d\eta}{(a_s^2 + r^2 - 2a_s r \eta)^{1/2}}$$

$$= -\frac{1}{a_s r}(r^2 + a_s^2 - 2a_s r \eta)^{1/2}\Big]_{\eta=-1}^{\eta=+1} = -\frac{1}{a_s r}\left[(r^2 + a_s^2 - 2a_s r)^{1/2} - (r^2 + a_s^2 + 2a_s r)^{1/2}\right]$$

Here in each of the two expressions under radicals in the last step the positive value of the square root has to be taken and hence we have two situations:

(i) $r > a_s$ viz. the point P lies **outside** the spherical shell (as shown in our figure). Here we have

$$I(a_s, r) = -\frac{1}{a_s r}[(r - a_s) - (r + a_s)] = +\frac{2}{r}$$

and accordingly

$$\vec{F}_{\text{Shell}} = \hat{r}\, G\, 2\pi a_s^2\, \sigma \frac{\partial}{\partial r} I(a_s, r) = \hat{r}\, G\, 2\pi\, a_s^2\, \sigma \frac{\partial}{\partial r}\left(\frac{z}{r}\right)$$

$$= -4\pi a_s^2\, \sigma \frac{G}{r^2}\hat{r} = -\frac{M_s G}{r^2}\hat{r} \qquad\qquad ...(4)$$

where $M_s = 4\pi a_s^2 \sigma$ is the mass of the spherical shell. Thus as far as points **outside** the spherical shell are concerned the gravitational field (force on a unit mass) is **as if** the entire mass of the shell were concentrated at the very centre of the spherical shell.

(*ii*) $r < a_s$ viz. the point P lies **inside** the spherical shell. Now again taking the positive root *i.e.*,

$(r^2 + a_s^2 - 2ra_s)^{1/2} = a_s - r$ and not $r - a_s$ as earlier, we have

$$I(a_s, r) = -\frac{1}{a_s r}\left[(a_s - r) - (r + a_s)\right] = \frac{2}{a_s}$$

and accordingly as $\dfrac{\partial}{\partial r} I(a_s, r) = 0$, we have

$$\vec{F}_{\text{Shell}} = 0$$

Thus for points **inside** the spherical shell the gravitational field is **zero**.

Because the earth, the moon, the planets and even the apple are nearly sperical bodies, let us consider the **Symmetric sphere**. Such bodies are spheres and their mass densities depend only on distance from the centre. For example the earth has a density of ~3000 kg/m^3 near its surface but its density near the centre is more than five times greater. We shall go on to show using our result on spherical shells that:

The gravitational force exerted by a symmetric sphere of mass M on a particle external to it is exactly the same as if the sphere were replaced by a particle of mass M located at its centre. This is because such a body may be considered to be composed of concentric spherical shells and each would act gravitationally on an external particle as if its mass were concentrated at the centre. Thus the resultant would be as if sum of all these masses, or in other words the total mass M of the symmetric sphere, were concentrated at the centre.

Since any element of mass is attracted by a symmetric sphere as if the sphere were a particle located at its centre, it follows that the force between two symmetric spheres of masses M_1 and M_2 with their centres located at $\vec{r}_1$ and $\vec{r}_2$ with $\vec{r}_1 - \vec{r}_2 = \vec{r}$ is given by

$$\vec{F} = -\hat{r}\frac{GM_1 M_2}{r^2} \qquad\qquad \text{...(5)}$$

and accordingly as far as the forces of gravitational attraction are concerned symmetric spheres behave exactly as if they were particles with the total masses concentrated at their respective centres.

Thus approximating the apple, the earth and other planets, the sun and the moon by symmetric spheres Newton was able to explain using his equation of motion and his law of universal gravitation the motion of the apple due to the attraction of the earth, the earth due to its attraction to the sun and the moon with respect to the earth and the planets around the sun. Each case was treated as a two body problem and the perturbation due to the other bodies were neglected in the lowest approximation. The results being in general agreement with observation justified the soundness of the underlying principles. Indeed, subsequently the concepts could be extended to other types of forces such as those of the electrostatic nature between charges and so on.

Section 3. THE TWO BODY PROBLEM: RELATIVE AND CENTRE OF MASS MOTIONS

If we have an isolated system of two particles of masses m_1 and m_2 located at $\vec{r}_1$ and $\vec{r}_2$ with respect to some coordinate system (as shown in Fig. 1), whatever be the nature of the force (gravitation or otherwise) we expect the force to depend on $\vec{r}_1 - \vec{r}_2$ and not on $\vec{r}_1$ and $\vec{r}_2$ separately, simply because this should not depend on our choice of origin of the coordinate system. Furthermore by virtue of the third law [see equations (2a) and (2b)] we may rewrite them as

$$m_1 \frac{d^2 \vec{r}_1}{dt^2} = \vec{F}_{1\leftarrow 2} = \vec{F} \qquad ...(6a)$$

$$m_2 \frac{d^2 \vec{r}_2}{dt^2} = \vec{F}_{2\leftarrow 1} = -\vec{F} \qquad ...(6b)$$

with

$$\vec{F}_{1\leftarrow 2} = -\vec{F}_{2\leftarrow 1} \equiv \vec{F}$$

Defining the centre of mass coordinate through

$$\vec{R} = \frac{m_1 \vec{r}_1 + m_2 \vec{r}_2}{m_1 + m_2} \qquad ...(7a)$$

and the relative coordinate by

$$\vec{r} = \vec{r}_1 - \vec{r}_2 \qquad ...(7b)$$

and adding equations (6a) and (6b) it is easy to see that

$$\frac{d^2}{dt^2} \vec{R} = 0 \qquad ...(8)$$

which tells us that the centre of mass coordinate does not accelerate and the force does not enter into its motion at all. Indeed $\vec{R}$ would move with uniform unchanging velocity and if we choose a coordinate frame in which $\frac{d\vec{R}}{dt}$ is zero (at rest) then it would remain at rest. This coordinate frame is known as the centre of mass system.

The non-trivial dynamics resides in the relative coordinate $\vec{r}$. Using equations (7a) and (7b) let us write $\vec{r}_1$ and $\vec{r}_2$ in terms of $\vec{r}$ and $\vec{R}$. This is readily done to yield

$$\vec{r}_1 = \vec{R} + \frac{m_2}{M} \vec{r} \qquad ...(9a)$$

$$\vec{r}_2 = \vec{R} - \frac{m_1}{M} \vec{r} \qquad ...(9b)$$

where we have introduced $M = m_1 + m_2$.

Noting that by virtue of equations (8) and (9a) $\dfrac{d^2}{dt^2}\vec{r}_1 = \dfrac{m_2}{M}\dfrac{d^2\vec{r}}{dt^2}$ we multiply by m_1 and use

equation (6a) and thereby get the non-trival dynamical equation for the relative motion

$$m\frac{d^2\vec{r}}{dt^2} = \left(\frac{m_1 m_2}{m_1 + m_2}\right)\frac{d^2\vec{r}}{dt^2} = \vec{F} \qquad \qquad ...(10)$$

$$\frac{m_1 m_2}{M} = \frac{m_1 m_2}{m_1 + m_2} \equiv m \text{ is known as the reduced mass.}$$

Section 4. CENTRAL FORCES AND THE CONSERVATION OF ANGULAR MOMENTUM

We have already seen (vide equation 2c) that for a system of two isolated particles the total momentum (also called linear momentum) is time-independent or conserved as a consequence of the third law.

Furthermore we have seen that between two point masses (or between two homogenous spherical bodies) the force between them is directed along the vector joining them (or their centres) viz. $\vec{F} = +F(r)\hat{r}$ with $F(r) = G\dfrac{m_1 m_2}{r^2}$ and the same in true for the electrostatic force between two point charges. Such forces are called central forces. Let us consider Newton's equation of motion for central forces

$$\frac{d\vec{p}}{dt} = \vec{F} = F(r)\hat{r} \qquad \qquad ...(11)$$

Consider now the vector $\vec{L} \equiv \vec{r} \times \vec{p}$ which is the vector product of the relative coordinate $\vec{r}$ and the momentum vector $\vec{p}$ (see Appendix IA to help you recall the elements of vector algebra). This vector $\vec{L}$ is perpendicular at any instant to the plane containing the vectors $\vec{r}$ and $\vec{p}$ and of magnitude $rp\sin\theta$ where r and p are the magnitude of $\vec{r}$ and $\vec{p}$ and θ is the angle between them. Now note that

$$\frac{d}{dt}\vec{L} = \frac{d}{dt}(\vec{r} \times \vec{p}) = \frac{d\vec{r}}{dt} \times \vec{p} + \vec{r} \times \frac{d\vec{p}}{dt} = 0 + \vec{r} \times \hat{r}F(r) = 0 \qquad ...(12)$$

where in the last but one step we note that $\dfrac{d\vec{r}}{dt} = \vec{p}/m$ by definition of momentum and thus $\dfrac{d\vec{r}}{dt} \times \vec{p} = 0$ as the cross or vector product of two vectors in the same direction ($\sin\theta = 0$) is zero and we have used Newton's equation (11) for a central force. Again in the last step we note that $\vec{r} \times \hat{r} = 0$ (as $\vec{r}$ and $\hat{r}$ are in the same direction). Thus we see that for a central force the angular momentum $\vec{L} = \vec{r} \times \vec{p}$ is conserved.

However, the force between two particles is not necessarily central. In the case of two point particles or homogeneous spheres the only physically relevant vector for the problem was the relative coordinate vector $\vec{r}$ and hence it is not surprising that the force $\vec{F}$ another vector should depend on $\vec{r}$. But if we consider for example the force between two magnetic dipoles $\vec{\mu}_1$ and $\vec{\mu}_2$ the force could very well and does depend on the relative orientations of the dipole moments as well. In general therefore all we can say is

$$\frac{d}{dt}\vec{L} = \frac{d}{dt}(\vec{r}\times\vec{p}) = \frac{d\vec{r}}{dt}\times\vec{p} + \vec{r}\times\frac{d\vec{p}}{dt} = \vec{r}\times\vec{F} = \vec{\tau} \qquad \dots(13)$$

where $\vec{\tau} \equiv \vec{r}\times\vec{F}$ is the torque or twist which causes a change in the angular momentum analogous to the force $\vec{F}$ that causes a change in the momentum.

Section 5. WORK AND THE CONCEPT OF ENERGY

To appreciate the notion of work and the related concept of energy it is wise to start with motion along a line viz. in one dimension. The Newton's equation of motion is

$$m\frac{d^2x}{dt^2} = F(x)$$

we have taken the force to be only a function of x, *i.e.*, it is time and velocity independent. Multiplying this equation by $\frac{dx}{dt}$ and integrate over time t_1 to t_2 when the particle is at x_1 and x_2 respectively we have

$$\int_{t_1}^{t_2} m\frac{dx}{dt}\frac{d^2x}{dt^2}dt = \int_{t_1}^{t_2} F(x)\frac{dx}{dt}dt = \int_{x_1}^{x_2} F(x)dx$$

which results in

$$\left[\frac{1}{2}m\left(\frac{dx}{dt}\right)^2\right]_{t_1}^{t_2} = \int_{x_1}^{x_2} F(x)dx \qquad \dots(14)$$

Now the quantity Fdx is known as the element of work done by the force on the particle during a displacement of the particle by dx. On the other hand $\frac{1}{2}m\left(\frac{dx}{dt}\right)^2 = \frac{1}{2}mv^2 = T$ is known as the kinetic energy of the particle that is the energy possessed by the particle by virtue of its motion. Thus equation (14) expressed the fact that the work done by the force on the particle in displacing it from x_1 to x_2 equals or goes into increasing the kinetic energy of the particle. Moreover if we write

$$F(x) = -\frac{dV(x)}{dx} \qquad \dots(15)$$

then $\int\limits_{x_1}^{x_2} F(x)dx = -\int\limits_{x_1}^{x_2} \dfrac{dV(x)}{dx} dx = -V(x_2)+V(x_1)$ and we may restate equation (14) as

$$T_1 + V(x_1) = T_2 + V(x_2) \qquad \ldots(16)$$

calling $V(x)$ the potential energy of the particle viz. its potential to do work then equation (16) is a statement which is known as the conservation of energy namely the sum of the kinetic and potential energies of a particle is a constant. This is so provided F is a function of x alone and not of time or velocity. Of course if we add a constant to the potential V equation (15) is still valid for the force and hence the potential is defined modulo an added constant. Thus one, may write the total energy

$$E = T + V(x) = \text{constant} \qquad \ldots(17)$$

In the next section we shall illustrate the ideas described above using various examples of motion in one dimension.

To generalise our considerations to three dimensions we begin with the equation of motion

$m\dfrac{d^2\vec{r}}{dt^2} = \vec{F}$ where $\vec{F}$ is a factors of (x, y, z) and not of time or velocity.

We take the scalar product with the velocity vector $\dfrac{d\vec{r}}{dt}$

$$m\dfrac{d\vec{r}}{dt} \cdot \dfrac{d^2\vec{r}}{dt^2} = \vec{F} \cdot \dfrac{d\vec{r}}{dt}$$

We integrate with respect to time to get

$$\left[\frac{1}{2}m\left(\dfrac{d\vec{r}}{dt}\right)^2 \right]_{t_1}^{t_2} = \int\limits_{t_1}^{t_2} \vec{F} \cdot \dfrac{d\vec{r}}{dt} dt = \int\limits_{\vec{r}_1}^{\vec{r}_2} \vec{F} \cdot d\vec{r} \qquad \ldots(18)$$

where $\vec{r}_1$ and $\vec{r}_2$ are the position vectors of the particle at times t_1 and t_2 respectively.

The left hand side is again simply the change in the kinetic energy suitably generalized to three dimensions. To interpret the right hand side we may claim that just as in one dimension Fdx was the element of work done by the force on the particle during a displacement dx of the particle, $\vec{F} \cdot d\vec{r}$ is the work done by the force $\vec{F}$ on the particle during a displacement $d\vec{r}$ of the particle. But here what is involved is the scalar product and we have $\vec{F} \cdot d\vec{r} = |\vec{F}| |d\vec{r}| \cos\theta$, where θ is the angle between the force and the displacement. Thus work is done only by the component of the force along the direction of the displacement. However, in the next step a problem arises. In one dimension the right hand side

$\int\limits_{x_1}^{x_2} F(x)dx$ could be written as $-V(x_2) + V(x_1)$ by putting $F(x) = -\dfrac{dV}{dx}$ and we had a result which only

depended on the end points x_1 and x_2 of the path of integration simply because in one dimension between two points there is only one way to go. But in three dimensions this is not necessarily so as

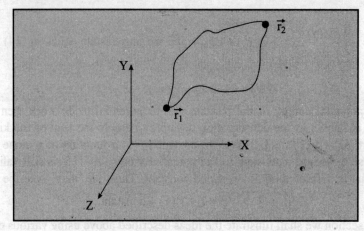

Fig. 3

there may be many paths from $\vec{r}_1$ to $\vec{r}_2$ and the integral may be path dependent. For this integral to be path independent it is essential that $\vec{F} \cdot d\vec{r} = -dV$ namely a perfect differential so that we may then

obtain $\int\limits_{\vec{r}_1}^{\vec{r}_2} \vec{F} \cdot d\vec{r} = -\int\limits_{\vec{r}_1}^{\vec{r}_2} dV = V(\vec{r}_1) - V(\vec{r}_2)$ and a conservation law for $E = T + V$ would result.

Now the infinitesimal change of a function $V(x, y, z)$ of more than one variable due to small changes in x, y and z may be written using partial derivatives as

$$dV = \frac{\partial V}{\partial x} dx + \frac{\partial V}{\partial y} dy + \frac{\partial V}{\partial z} dz \qquad \text{...(19a)}$$

where $\dfrac{\partial V}{\partial x}$ is the differential of V with respect to x holding y and z constant and so on. Note that the right hand side of equation (19a) may be written as the scalar product of two vectors

$$\vec{\nabla} V = \hat{i} \frac{\partial V}{\partial x} + \hat{j} \frac{\partial V}{\partial y} + \hat{k} \frac{\partial V}{\partial z} \qquad \text{...(19b)}$$

and

$$d\vec{r} = \hat{i} dx + \hat{j} dy + \hat{k} dz \qquad \text{...(19c)}$$

where $\hat{i}, \hat{j}, \hat{k}$ are unit vectors along x, y and z respectively. The left hand side of equation (19b) is

mererly a convenient notation by introducing a vectorial differential operator $\vec{\nabla} = \hat{i} \dfrac{\partial}{\partial x} + \hat{j} \dfrac{\partial}{\partial y} + \hat{k} \dfrac{\partial}{\partial z}$ which acting on a scalar function such as V gives us a vectorial quantity. Thus we conclude that we can also define a conserved energy (kinetic plus potential) in three dimensions provided the force can be written as the negative gradient of a potential function

$$\vec{F} = -\vec{\nabla} V \qquad \text{...(20)}$$

and a force that can be so written is known as a conservative force. Recalling that the gravitational force on a homogeneous spherical body of mass m whose centre is at a distance r from the centre of another homogeneous spherical body of mass M is given by

$$\vec{F} = -\frac{Gm\,M\vec{r}}{r^3} = -\frac{Gm\,M\hat{r}}{r^2}$$

where $\hat{r}$ is the unit vector along $\vec{r}$, we note that

$$\vec{\nabla}\frac{1}{r} = \hat{i}\frac{\partial}{\partial x}\left(\frac{1}{r}\right) + \hat{j}\frac{\partial}{\partial y}\left(\frac{1}{r}\right) + \hat{k}\frac{\partial}{\partial z}\left(\frac{1}{r}\right)$$

$$= -\hat{i}\frac{x}{r^3} - \hat{j}\frac{y}{r^3} - \hat{k}\frac{z}{r^3} = -i\frac{\vec{r}}{r^3}$$

as $\dfrac{\partial}{\partial x}\left(\dfrac{1}{r}\right) = \dfrac{\partial}{\partial x}\dfrac{1}{\sqrt{x^2 + y^2 + z^2}} = -\dfrac{1}{2}\dfrac{1}{(x^2 + y^2 + z^2)^{3/2}} \cdot 2x = -\dfrac{x}{r^3}$ and so on.

Thus we may assert that

$$\vec{F} = -\vec{\nabla}V \qquad \qquad \ldots(21a)$$

where
$$V = -\frac{GmM}{r} \qquad \qquad \ldots(21b)$$

Thus the gravitational potential energy of such a particle of mass m at a distance r from the centre of a spherically symmetric body of mass M is given by equation $(21b)$; and the gravitational force is a conservative force.

Section 6. ILLUSTRATIVE PROBLEMS IN ONE AND TWO DIMENSIONAL MOTION

·In order to consolidate the understanding of the concepts developed so far we begin with the simplest of problems involving motion in one dimension.

Free particle

A free particle of mass m is one on which no forces are acting and hence

$$m\frac{d^2x}{dt^2} = 0$$

$$\frac{dx}{dt} = \text{constant} = u\,(\text{say})$$

$$x = ut + x_0$$

where x_0 is the location of the particle at $t = 0$ and u, a constant, is the velocity with which it moves.

The momentum of the particle $p = m\dfrac{dx}{dt} = mu$ is a constant.

The particle only possesses kinetic energy $E = \dfrac{1}{2}mu^2 = \dfrac{p^2}{2m}$ which is constant.

Particle acted upon by a constant force

Consider a particle of mass m moving in one dimension under the influence of a constant (position x independent) force F. Here x represents the distance of the particle from a fixed origin. Thus the velocity of the particle at any fixed instant of time t is $\dfrac{dx}{dt}$. Hence the momentum of the particle at that instant is $p = m\dfrac{dx}{dt}$. Therefore, by Newton's Equation of Motion, we have:

$$\frac{dp}{dt} = m\frac{d}{dt}\frac{dx}{dt} = m\frac{d^2x}{dt^2} = F$$

Since the force F is a constant $\dfrac{F}{m} \equiv f$ is also a constant. Hence the particle moves with a constant acceleration $\dfrac{dv}{dt} = \dfrac{d^2x}{dt^2} = \dfrac{F}{m} = f$, where $v = \dfrac{dx}{dt}$ is the velocity at any instant of time. Thus $\dfrac{dv}{dt} = f$ which when integrated over t gives $v = ft + \text{constant}$. If the velocity of the particle has the value u at time $t = 0$ (initial condition), then the constant is readily seen to be u and hence

$$v = \frac{dx}{dt} = u + ft$$

Thus we see that the velocity increases linearly with time.

To find how the position x changes with time we integrate again with respect to time to get

$$x = ut + \frac{1}{2}ft^2 + \text{constant}$$

If the particle was initially (at $t = 0$) located at $x = x_0$ then the constant of integration is seen to be x_0 and thus

$$x = x_0 + ut + \frac{1}{2}ft^2$$

Particle falling freely under gravity near the earth's surface

Consider a particle of mass m near and above the earth's surface (let us say at a height z above the earth's surface). Let us take the z-axis as vertically upwards. Approximating the earth as a symmetric sphere of mass M_E and radius R_E by virtue of the Newton's Universal Law of Gravitation the force acting on the particle is given by

$$\vec{F} = -\frac{Gm\,M_E}{(R_E + z)^2}\hat{z}$$

where $\hat{z}$ is the unit vector pointing upwards. Since the particle is near the earth's surface ($z \ll R_E$) and accordingly to a very good approximation $R_E + z \approx R_E$ we may write

$$\vec{F} \simeq -\frac{GmM_E}{R_E^2}\hat{z} \equiv -mg\hat{z} \qquad \qquad ...(22)$$

where we have introduced the constant

$$g \equiv \frac{GM_E}{R_E^2} = \frac{[6.67\times10^{-11}\text{m}^3\,\text{sec}^{-2}(\text{kg})^{-1}]\times[6\times10^{24}\,\text{kg}]}{(6.4\times10^6\,\text{m})^2} \simeq 9.81\,\text{m/sec}^2$$

putting in the values for G, M_E and R_E in the **MKS** system of units.

By virtue of Newton's Equation of Motion we have for a particle near the earth's surface

$$m\frac{d^2z}{dt^2} = -mg \quad \Rightarrow \quad \frac{d^2z}{dt^2} = -g \qquad \qquad ...(23)$$

This implies that the acceleration due to the earth's gravitational attraction on **all** falling bodies (if sufficiently near the earth's surface) is g downwards. Therefore, naturally g is known as the acceleration due to gravity. However, since the earth is not really a symmetric sphere but only approximately so, there are small variations in g_{actual} from place to place which for our present purposes we neglect and adopt for convenience a standard value $g = 9.81$ m/sec^2.

Thus if a body is dropped from rest at a height $z = h$ from the ground the integral of $\dfrac{d^2z}{dt^2} = -g$

yields $\dfrac{dz}{dt} = -gt + $ constant but as at $t = 0$ the particle dropped (viz. have velocity zero) the constant is

zero by imposing the initial condition or $\dfrac{dz}{dt} = -gt$. Integrating again with respect to t, we get

$z = -\dfrac{1}{2}gt^2 + $ constant and since at $t = 0$, $z = h$

we have

$$z = h - \frac{1}{2}gt^2 \quad \text{and} \quad v = -gt \qquad \qquad ...(24)$$

The time taken to hit the ground ($z = 0$) is $t = \sqrt{\dfrac{2h}{g}}$ and the velocity when it hits the ground is

$v = -g\sqrt{\dfrac{2h}{g}} = -\sqrt{2hg}$ the minus sign indicates that the velocity is downwards.

It is also worthwhile analysing the problem from the basic energetics. Since the force is $\vec{F} = -mg\hat{z}$

the potential energy is given by $-\int \vec{F}\cdot d\vec{r} = +\displaystyle\int_{z_0}^{z} mgdz$ as $\vec{F}\cdot d\vec{r} = Fdz$ as $d\vec{r} = \hat{i}dx + \hat{j}dy + \hat{k}dz$. The

arbitrary addition constant in the potential energy may be fixed by choosing z_0 for example, to be zero so that potential energy is being measured with respect to the ground as being chosen as the place when we shall take it to be zero by convention. We use vector notation to familiarize the student with one dimensional motion in the more general setting.

Thus
$$V(z) = \int_0^z mg\,dz = mgz \qquad \qquad ...(25)$$

where z is the height of the particle above ground level. The kinetic energy of the falling body on the other hand is given by

$$T = \frac{1}{2}m\dot{z}^2 \qquad \qquad ...(26)$$

and thus the total energy of the falling body at any height z above the ground is given by

$$E = T + V = \frac{1}{2}m\dot{z}^2 + mgz$$

$$= \frac{1}{2}mg^2t^2 + mg\left(h - \frac{1}{2}gt^2\right) = mgh \qquad \qquad ...(27)$$

through the use of equation (24); at time $t = 0$ as the body is dropped from a height h, the kinetic energy is zero, the potential energy is mgh the total energy is mgh. As the particle falls the kinetic energy grows at the expense of the potential energy, the sum remaining constant. As it reaches the ground via

our choice of standard the potential energy is zero and all the energy is kinetic $\frac{1}{2}mv^2 = mgh$ and so

$v = \sqrt{2gh}$. Indeed energy conservation is useful to arrive at quick results.

Falling body with viscosity taken into account

The situation is rather different when we take into account the frictional force arising from the effect of air resistance through viscosity. The force of viscosity is proportional to the velocity of the body moving through a fluid as also on its size and shape and always opposes the motion. Thus the viscous force on a spherical object of radius a moving through a fluid of viscosity η is given by $-6\pi\eta a\vec{v}$ (this result was derived by Stokes using fluid dynamics). We shall take the force of viscosity to be $-\gamma\vec{v}$. Thus the equation of motion of a body of mass m falling under the combined action of the earth's gravity and air resistance is most conveniently written in terms of the vertical component, velocity measured positive downwards

$$m\frac{dv}{dt} = mg - \gamma v \qquad \qquad ...(28)$$

Rewriting this in the form

$$\frac{dv}{v - \frac{mg}{\gamma}} = -\frac{\gamma}{m}dt$$

and integrating from $t = 0$ to t we have

$$\int_{v(t=0)=0}^{v(t)} \frac{dv}{v - \frac{mg}{\gamma}} = -\frac{\gamma}{m} \int_0^t dt$$

$$\log_e \left[v(t) - \frac{mg}{\gamma} \right] - \log_e \left[-\frac{mg}{\gamma} \right] = -\frac{\gamma t}{m}$$

where at time $t = 0$, since the particle is dropped from rest, we have $v(t = 0) = 0$. Thus

$$\log_e \left(\frac{-v(t) + \frac{mg}{\gamma}}{+\frac{mg}{\gamma}} \right) = -\frac{\gamma t}{m}$$

resulting in the solution

$$v = +\frac{mg}{\gamma}(1 - e^{-\gamma t/m}) \qquad \qquad ...(29)$$

Note that as $t \to \infty$, $e^{-\gamma t/m} \to 0$ and $v \to -\frac{gm}{\gamma}$. This is known as the terminal velocity. The negative sign is simply because we are taking positive upwards. Thus in the limit with the increase in speed of the falling object the gravitational force becomes equal and opposite to the frictional force $\gamma |v| = mg$ and

we have $|v| = +\frac{gm}{\gamma}$. Thus at the terminal velocity there is no net force acting on the body.

In this case, the potential and kinetic energies of the falling body when added together is not a constant. This is because the viscous force is not conservative (being here velocity dependent). The reason for this apparent loss of energy is because the falling body is dissipating some of its energy through viscosity into the medium through which it is moving. The total energy taking the medium into account as well is a constant.

Sliding down an inclined plane

Discuss the motion of a block of mass m sliding down a fixed incline making an angle θ with the horizontal. Here suppose that the coefficient of friction between the block and the inclined surface is μ. Find also the angle of repose θ_r (where the block shall remain at rest on the incline despite gravity given that the coefficient of static friction is μ_s).

General approach: Draw a clear diagram. See how the body whose motion is to be studied can be treated as a particle. Choose coordinates for the particle. Determine all the forces acting on the particle including the forces which constrain the body in any way. Write out Newton's Equation of Motion and solve with the given initial conditions.

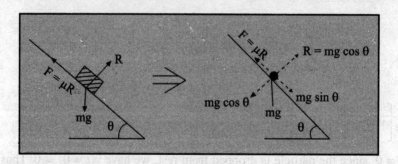

Fig. 3a

The forces on the particle representing the block are:

(*i*) the force of gravity *mg* vertically downwards

(*ii*) the force of reaction of the inclined plane *R* perpendicular to the plane; this force is a force of constraint which is exactly balanced by the component of the force of gravity perpendicular to the plane. As long as the block is in contact with the incline the net force acting on the block at right angles to the inclined plane must be zero, as there is no motion along that direction. Thus

$$R = mg \cos \theta$$

(*iii*) the other component of the force of gravity *mg* sin θ acting down the plane remains unbalanced as it is this that causes the slide down the incline.

(*iv*) the slide, however, is opposed by the force of friction offered by the inclined plane to the block caused by the roughness of their surface of contact; this force opposes the motion and if the block is sliding down acts up the incline, and is proportional to the reaction

$$F = \mu R = \mu \, mg \cos \theta$$

where the constant of proportionality μ depending on the nature (roughness) of the surfaces is known as the coefficient of friction.

As for the coordinate to be chosen it is but natural to take it to be the distance *s* down the incline as this problem is basically one dimensional and that is the dynamical variable.

Thus the net force acting down slope which is responsible for the acceleration causing sliding is *mg* sin θ – μ*mg* cos θ and, therefore, by Newton's Equation of Motion we have

$$m\frac{d^2 s}{dt^2} = mg(\sin\theta - \mu\cos\theta)$$

where *s* is the distance down the slope from the starting point. Note, however, that this is true only if

$$\sin\theta > \mu\cos\theta$$

so that we are considering the situation where the block is sliding down the slope. If, on the other hand, the block had been initially given a push up-slope with an initial velocity $v = \frac{ds}{dt}$ at time *t* = 0, then when moving upwards it would face an acceleration downslope (actually a deceleration)

$$g(\sin \theta + \mu \cos \theta)$$

as both the components of gravity along the incline and the force of friction (always opposing motion) would be downslope. In this latter situation, however, this would hold with block moving up slope till it comes to rest and after that the block would begin to slide down as discussed earlier. The solution of the differential equations with the constants of integration to be determined through the imposition of initial conditions is left as an exercise for the student.

A limiting situation is one in which the block left at rest on the incline would remain at rest. In such a circumstance the slope of the incline should be such that the component of gravity down-slope is able to balance the force of friction $\mu_s R = \mu_s \, mg \cos\theta$, where μ_s is coefficient of static friction (the force of friction could very well and does depend on the state of motion of the surfaces concerned). The angle of repose θ_r of the inclined plane would, therefore, be given by

$$g \sin \theta_r = \mu_s \cos\theta_r$$

and for an incline with slope $\theta < \theta_r$ where $\theta_r = \tan^{-1}(\mu_s/g)$ the force of friction (which is self-adjusting) is able to keep such a block kept on the slope at rest to remain at rest.

The Atwood's machine

The Atwood's Machine is a contraption (or device) where two masses m_1 and m_2 are joined by a mass–less and inextensible string which passes over a fixed and mass–less pulley as shown in the diagram below. In the idealized situation we neglect frictional forces. We shall describe the motion below.

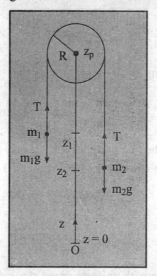

Fig. 3b

We have shown the pulley with some radius R, the centre of which is located at the fixed point z_p with the coordinate z measured vertically upwards from some origin marked O. The coordinate of the particle of mass m_1 is designated by z_1 and that of mass m_2 by z_2. It is readily seen from the diagram that the total length of the string is given by

$$l = (z_p - z_1) + (z_p - z_2) + \pi R$$

and since the string is inextensible and R and z_p are fixed we have $z_1 + z_2 = $ constant. Furthermore the effect of the force of gravity on the two masses would tend to stretch the string and since the string is inextensible this implies that there is a force of constraint which is the tension of the string shown as T. With z measured upwards the Newton's equations of motion for the two particles are

$$m_2 \frac{d^2 z_2}{dt^2} = -m_2 g + T$$

$$m_1 \frac{d^2 z_1}{dt^2} = -m_1 g + T$$

The fact that the string is inextensible implies as we have already seen that $z_1 + z_2 = $ constant

which in turn implies that $\frac{d}{dt}(z_1 + z_2) = 0$ and $\frac{d^2}{dt^2}(z_1 + z_2) = 0$ and thus $\frac{d^2 z_2}{dt^2} = -\frac{d^2 z_1}{dt^2}$ and therefore

the two equations above may be re-written as

$$m_2 \frac{d^2 z_1}{dt^2} = m_2 g - T$$

$$m_1 \frac{d^2 z_1}{dt^2} = m_1 g + T$$

adding the two equations and dividing by $m_1 + m_2$ tells us that

$$\frac{d^2 z_1}{dt^2} = \frac{m_2 - m_1}{m_1 + m_2} g \quad \text{and thus} \quad \frac{d^2 z_2}{dt^2} = +\frac{m_1 - m_2}{m_1 + m_2} g$$

Knowing the accelerations of the two particles it is an easy matter to find out about the motion of the system. The tension of the string (the force of constraint T) is also readily determined to be

$$T = \frac{2 m_1 m_2}{m_1 + m_2} g$$

Uniform circular motion

Consider a particle of mass m moving with uniform speed along a fixed circle of radius a. This may be, for example, the system comprising of a bead threaded into a circular hoop of radius a which though constrained to move along this circle is otherwise free.

Though the motion is in two dimensions we shall see that it effective requires but one dynamical variable for its description. Let us say the particle moves anti-clockwise along the circle with constant angular velocity ω. Starting at $t = 0$ from the point $x = R$, $y = 0$ as shown in the figure as follows:

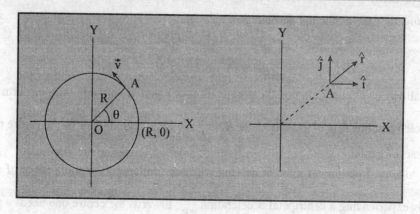

Fig. 3c

After a time t the particle will have moved to point A having traversed an angle $\theta = \omega t$. The position of the particle can then be described by

$$x(t) = R \cos \omega t$$
$$y(t) = R \sin \omega t$$

or by the vector $\vec{r} = \hat{i} x(t) + \hat{j} y(t)$ where $\hat{i}$ and $\hat{j}$ are unit vectors along the X and Y axes. Note that $r = |\vec{r}| = R$, the velocity of the particle at A is described by the vector $\vec{v}(t) = \dfrac{d}{dt} \vec{r}(t) = v_x \hat{i} + v_y \hat{j}$ where

$$v_x(t) = \frac{dx(t)}{dt} = -R\omega \sin \omega t$$

$$v_y(t) = \frac{dy(t)}{dt} = R\omega \cos \omega t$$

Note that the magnitude of the vector $\vec{v}$, viz , $v = \sqrt{v_x^2 + v_y^2} = r\omega$, which makes sense because in unit time the angle swept out is ω and as this is in radians, the length of the arc swept out along the circle in unit time is $R\omega$ which is accordingly the speed along the path of the particle. Also observe that the scalar product

$$\vec{r} \cdot \vec{v} = xv_x + yv_y = 0$$

which implies that $\vec{v}$ is orthogonal to $\vec{r}$ as indicated in the figure. The velocity is tangential to the circle which is of course normal to the radius vector at A. We go on to calculate the acceleration $\dfrac{d^2 \vec{r}}{dt^2} = \dfrac{d\vec{v}}{dt}$ the components of which are

$$\frac{d^2 x}{dt^2} = \frac{d}{dt} v_x = -R\omega^2 \cos \omega t = -\omega^2 x$$

$$\frac{d^2 y}{dt^2} = \frac{d}{dt} v_y = -R\omega^2 \sin \omega t = -\omega^2 y$$

which put together yields for the acceleration

$$\frac{d^2\vec{r}}{dt^2} = -\omega^2\vec{r}$$

This allows us to conclude that the acceleration of a particle moving with uniform speed $v = \omega R$ along a circle of radius R is of magnitude $\omega^2 R = \frac{v^2}{R}$ and is directed towards the centre of the circle, a centripetal acceleration.

Thus to keep a particle of mass m moving with uniform speed v along a circle of radius R, or in other words experiencing a centripetal acceleration $\frac{v^2}{R}$ towards the centre one needs a force to **cause** this. In the case of the bead on the hoop this force is provided by the reaction of the wire on the bead. This force of constraint must be of magnitude mv^2/R in accordance to Newton's equation of motion to keep the bead moving as described.

Another such example is provided by a stone tied to an inextensible string twirled around such that the stone turns about in a circle with uniform speed. Here the centripetal force causing the centripetal acceleration (v^2/R) is provided by the tension of the string $T = mv^2/R$ giving the equation of balance.

A third example is the motion of the moon around the earth. While the motion of two bodies caused by the gravitational force between them, in general results in various types of orbits which are conic sections (ellipses, parabolic and hyperbolic as we shall see later), a special case is the circle, which seems to be approximately the case for the motion of the moon around the earth. Here the cause of the centripetal acceleration of the moon v^2/R is the inverse square force of gravitation due to the earth. We shall return to this problem when we discuss relative motion between two such bodies.

Escape velocity from the surface of a symmetric sphere

Consider a projectile of mass m projected vertically upwards from the surface of a heavy symmetric sphere of mass M and radius R. What should be a minimum velocity of projection such that the projectile never returns?

Measuring vertical distances from the centre of the symmetric sphere as z, at the surface one has $z = R$. From this point on the surface suppose a projectile is shot upwards with initial velocity u at time $t = 0$. Since here we are anticipating situations where the projectile may not return we are not justified in using our earlier approximation of small heights and the constant force. Here the full glory of the inverse square law of gravitation must be employed.

The Newton's equation of motion is

$$m\frac{d^2z}{dt^2} = -\frac{mMG}{z^2}$$

which must be solved with the initial condition $\frac{dz}{dt} = u$ at $t = 0$. Let us try to find the maximum height z_{max} attained for a given initial velocity u. Clearly at z_{max} we shall have $\frac{dz}{dt} = 0$ for after that the projectile shall begin to fall back again reversing the direction of its velocity. The Newton's equation is easily integrated by first multiplying it by $\dfrac{dz}{dt}$ to get

$$m\left(\frac{dz}{dt}\right)\frac{d^2z}{dt^2} = -\frac{mMG}{z^2}\frac{dz}{dt}$$

and integrating with respect to time t. As for the left hand side we note that $\dfrac{d}{dt}\left[\dfrac{1}{2}\left(\dfrac{dz}{dt}\right)^2\right] = \dfrac{dz}{dt}\dfrac{d^2z}{dt^2}$ and

hence we have

$$\frac{1}{2}m\left(\frac{dz}{dt}\right)^2 = -\int\frac{mMG}{z^2}\frac{dz}{dt}dt = -mGM\int\frac{dz}{z^2} = +\frac{mGM}{z} + \text{constant}$$

or

$$\frac{1}{2}m\left(\frac{dz}{dt}\right)^2 - \frac{mGM}{z} = \text{constant} \equiv E$$

This result has the physical meaning that the sum of the kinetic energy $\dfrac{1}{2}m\left(\dfrac{dz}{dt}\right)^2$ and the

gravitational potential energy $-\dfrac{mGM}{z}$ is the total energy of the projectile which is a constant. At the

time of the launching ($t = 0$) the velocity is u and the potential energy is $-\dfrac{mMG}{R}$ (where R = radius of

the sphere).

Thus we have

$$\frac{1}{2}mu^2 - \frac{mMG}{R} = E$$

On the other hand when the projectile attains its maximum height z_{max} we have $\dfrac{dz}{dt} = 0$ (the

velocity and hence the kinetic energy is zero). Thus $-\dfrac{mMG}{z_{max}} = E$. Equating these two expressions for

the total energy we have

$$u = \sqrt{\left(\frac{MG}{R} - \frac{MG}{z_{max}}\right)^2}$$

Therefore, using this formula, given the values of M and R (and of course that of G) for a known initial velocity of upward launch of a projectile we can easily determine the maximum height it would attain before being pulled back again. We have however neglected for simplicity the viscosity of the atmosphere around.

We may also obtain the escape velocity, that is the minimum velocity with which to launch a projectile from a parent symmetric sphere of mass M and radius R such that it never returns. This is obtained by putting $z_{max} \rightarrow \infty$ such that

$$u_{escape} = \sqrt{\frac{MG}{R}}$$

As the body escapes to infinity the potential and kinetic energies would each tend to zero. At launch note that the kinetic and potential energies of the projectile are equal in magnitude and opposite in sign. In the case of the earth putting in values of M_E and R_E and noting that $\dfrac{GM_E}{R_E^2} = g$, the acceleration due to gravity at the earth's surface, we have $u_{escape} = \sqrt{2gR_E}$

$= \sqrt{2 \times 9.8 \text{ m/sec}^2 \times 6.4 \times 10^6 \text{ m}} = 1.1 \times 10^4$ m/sec.

The simple harmonic oscillator

Perhaps the most important problem in one-dimensional motion is the harmonic or linear oscillator. A particle of mass m moving solely under the action of an ideal massless spring which when extended or compressed from its relaxed position exerts a restoring force proportion to that displacement viz.

$$F = -kx$$

Under the influence of such a force the motion of the particles is governed by the Newton's equation

$$m\frac{d^2x}{dt^2} = -kx \qquad \qquad ...(30)$$

Putting $\dfrac{k}{m} = \omega^2$ this equation becomes

$$\frac{d^2x}{dt^2} = -\omega^2 x \qquad \qquad ...(31)$$

where $\omega = \sqrt{\dfrac{k}{m}}$. The solutions of this equation are easily seen to be $A \cos \omega t$ or $B \sin \omega t$ or infact any combination (sum) of these two because the equation is linear. This is something one must emphasise.

If x_1 and x_2 are two solution of equation (31) viz. $\dfrac{d^2x_1}{dt^2} = -\omega^2 x_1$ and $\dfrac{d^2x_2}{dt^2} = -\omega^2 x_2$ then any linear combination of these two viz. $c_1x_1 + c_2x_2$ where c_1 and c_2 are constants is also a solution of the equation. This is called the principle of linear superposition. The two as yet arbitrary constants will be fixed by the initial conditions.

Having discussed the solutions (which will be further investigated in our chapter on vibrations) we shall turn our attention to energetics. Multiplying the equation of motion [equation (30)] by $\dfrac{dx}{dt}$ we obtain $m\dfrac{dx}{dt}\dfrac{d^2x}{dt^2}=-kx\dfrac{dx}{dt}$ which when integrated over t yields $\dfrac{1}{2}m\left(\dfrac{dx}{dt}\right)^2=-k\displaystyle\int x\dfrac{dx}{dt}dt$

$=-k\displaystyle\int xdx=-\dfrac{k}{2}x^2+\text{constant}$ or $\dfrac{1}{2}m\left(\dfrac{dx}{dt}\right)^2+\dfrac{k}{2}x^2=$ constant. Now $\dfrac{1}{2}m\left(\dfrac{dx}{dt}\right)^2$ is nothing but the

kinetic energy of the particle. The potential energy is given by $V(x)=-\displaystyle\int_{x_0}^{x} Fdx$ where x_0 is some

standard displacement where we may take $V(x_0) = 0$. It is natural to take $x_0 = 0$ viz. the unstretched or uncompressed relaxed spring to have zero potential energy and thus

$$V(x) =-\int_0^x Fdx = \int_0^x kxdx =\frac{1}{2}kx^2 \qquad\qquad ...(32)$$

Thus the result that

$$\frac{1}{2}m\left(\frac{dx}{dt}\right)^2+\frac{k}{2}x^2 = \text{constant} = E \qquad\qquad ...(33)$$

is perfectly reasonable in that the sum of the kinetic and potential energies is a constant which is the conserved total energy.

Let us for concreteness adopt the solution

$$x = A \cos \omega t \qquad\qquad ...(34a)$$

Note here that at $t = 0$ we have $x = A$ and as

$$\dot{x} =-A\omega\sin \omega t \qquad\qquad ...(34b)$$

we have $\dot{x}=0$. Thus we have the maximum extension of the spring in the positive x-direction by an amount A which is known as the **amplitude** of the motion. Observe that at $t = 0$, for this particular solution, the kinetic energy $\dfrac{1}{2}m\dot{x}^2$ is zero while the potential energy $\dfrac{1}{2}kx^2$ is $\dfrac{1}{2}kA^2$. Thus the total energy is $\dfrac{1}{2}kA^2$. However at time $t=\dfrac{\pi}{2\omega}$ we have $\omega t =\dfrac{\pi}{2}$ and thus $x = 0$ and hence the potential energy $\dfrac{1}{2}kx^2 = 0$ and the kinetic energy $\dfrac{1}{2}m\dot{x}^2 =\dfrac{1}{2}m\omega^2 A^2 =\dfrac{1}{2}kA^2$ so that while at $t = 0$ the entire energy was potential, at $t =\dfrac{\pi}{2\omega}$ the entire energy is kinetic and the potential energy is zero (as at $x = 0$ the spring is relaxed). Here the kinetic energy is a maximum. At $t =\dfrac{\pi}{\omega}$ we have $x = -A$ and again the kinetic energy is zero and the potential energy a maximum and at $t=\dfrac{3\pi}{2\omega}$ we have $T =\dfrac{1}{2}m\dot{x}^2 =\dfrac{1}{2}m\omega^2 A^2 =\dfrac{1}{2}kA^2$ and $V = 0$ and we go back to $x = A$ when $t =\dfrac{2\pi}{\omega}$ having completed a cycle in the time period $\dfrac{2\pi}{\omega}$ of a complete oscillation which goes on and on.

Motion of a projectile near the earth's surface

Consider the motion of a projectile with mass m fired with initial speed u at an angle θ with respect to the horizontal plane. Choosing the z-direction as vertically upwards and the x-axis in the direction in which the projectile is aimed. We shall use the law of mechanics to determine the trajectory as shown in Fig. 4.

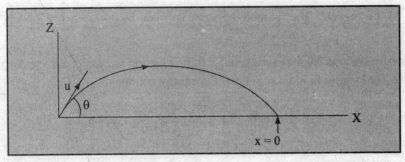

Fig. 4

We disregard the effect of the viscosity of air and also the fact that a frame of reference fixed to a point on the earth is not truly an inertial frame because the earth itself is rotating about its axis once in twenty four hours. The Newton's equation of motion is thus

$$m\frac{d^2\vec{r}}{dt^2} = -mg\hat{k}$$

where $\hat{k}$ is the unit vector along the z-axis. This must be solved with the initial conditions that at $t = 0$ we have $\vec{r} = 0$ and $\dfrac{d\vec{r}}{dt} = \vec{u}$. Concentrating on components along the x-and z-axis we have

$$\frac{d^2z}{dt^2} = -g \qquad \text{...(35a)}$$

$$\frac{d^2x}{dt^2} = 0 \qquad \text{...(35b)}$$

with the conditions that at $t = 0$, we have

$$x(t = 0) = 0 = z\,(t = 0) \qquad \text{...(35c)}$$

and $\qquad \dfrac{dx}{dt}(t = 0) = u\cos\theta \quad \text{and} \quad \dfrac{dz}{dt}(t = 0) = u\sin\theta \qquad \text{...(35d)}$

Integrating equations (35a) and (35b) we obtain

$$\frac{dz}{dt} = -gt + \text{constant}$$

$$\frac{dx}{dt} = \text{constant}$$

These constants of integration are fixed by imposing the initial condition (35d) to yield

$$\frac{dz}{dt} = -gt + u\sin\theta$$

$$\frac{dx}{dt} = u\cos\theta$$

We integrate once more to get

$$z = -\frac{1}{2}gt^2 + (u\sin\theta)t + \text{constant}$$

$$x = (u\cos\theta)t + \text{constant}$$

Again the constant of integration are fixed by imposing the initial conditions (35c) to yield

$$z = (u\sin\theta)t - \frac{1}{2}gt^2 \qquad\qquad ...(36a)$$

$$x = (u\cos\theta)t \qquad\qquad ...(36b)$$

The trajectory, that is the path traced out by the projectile in the xz-plane is found by eliminating the time t between these two equations. From (36b) $t = \dfrac{x}{u\cos\theta}$ which may be inserted in equation (36a) to obtain

$$z = (\tan\theta)x - \frac{g}{2u^2}(\sec^2\theta)x^2$$

which is the equation of a parabola which intersects the x-axis at $x = 0$ (the initial point of projection)

and at $x = u^2\dfrac{2\sin\theta\cos\theta}{g} = \dfrac{u^2\sin 2\theta}{g}$ the range, and the maximum height achieved occurs where $\dfrac{dz}{dx} = 0$

or $x = \dfrac{u^2}{g}\sin\theta\cos\theta$ and the maximum height is $z_{max} = \dfrac{u^2}{2g}\sin^2\theta$.

Some of these results follow in a much simpler manner by using the principle of energy conservation. Thus at the point of launching $x = z = 0$ the potential energy is zero (as it is at ground level) and the

kinetic energy is $\dfrac{1}{2}mu^2$. The total energy is $\dfrac{1}{2}mu^2$. At the highest point of the trajectory the component

of $\vec{u}$ along z must be zero and that along x must be the same as at the point of launching (as there is no

force along the X-direction), hence $u\cos\theta$. Thus the kinetic energy there is $\dfrac{1}{2}mu^2\cos^2\theta$. The potential

energy at that point is mgz_{max}. Thus the total energy at this highest point in the trajectory is

$mgz_{max} + \dfrac{1}{2}mu^2\cos^2\theta$. Thus by energy conservation $mgz_{max} + \dfrac{1}{2}mu^2\cos^2\theta = \dfrac{1}{2}mu^2$ or

$mgz_{max} = \dfrac{1}{2}mu^2(1 - \cos^2\theta) = \dfrac{1}{2}mu^2\sin^2\theta$ and thus $z_{max} = \dfrac{u^2}{2g}\sin^2\theta$. Indeed as we shall see in

Chapter 2 the introduction of the Lagrangian and the Hamiltonian enables us to deal with systems in a much more efficient manner where we shall not be encumbered by vectors, components, constraints etc.

Problems involving collisions

The generics of collision between bodies can often be analysed at a basic level by simply applying conservation laws. This level of description may be termed as kinematics. Detailed dynamics however would depend on the forces acting between them. In collision problems the particles move, when far away from each other, before and after they interact, as free particles with constant velocity (and momentum). Of course they come closer, interact with each other, but if the mutual forces during collision satisfy Newton's third law then the total linear momentum of the two particles colliding is the same before and after the collision. Thus we may with confidence impose the conservation of momentum.

As far as energy conservation is concerned if the bodies that collide are ideal particles (point objects with no internal degrees of freedom) then their total initial kinetic energy when they are far away from each other (mutual interactions negligible) must be the same as their total final kinetic energy when again they are far away from each other after collision (mutual interactions negligible). Such collisions are called **elastic** collisions where the total kinetic energy is also conserved. First we shall consider such collisions and later discuss the possibilities of *inelastic* collisions between bodies that have internal degrees of freedom such that they may eat up some energy to get excited or deliver some energy in getting de-excited.

Let us then consider the collision of particle of mass m_1 and momentum $\vec{p}_1$ with a particle of mass m_2 at rest. Let the particle of mass m_1 be '**scattered**' through an angle θ (see Fig. 5).

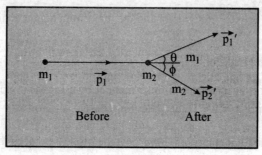

Fig. 5

Clearly we need concern ourselves only with the plane of scattering because the only force that causes the phenomenon is that between the particles. Thus momentum conservation dictates that

$$\vec{p}_1 = \vec{p}_1' + \vec{p}_2' \qquad\qquad ...(37a)$$

as $\vec{p}_2 = 0$ (the second particle is initially at rest).

Looking at components along and perpendicular to $\vec{p}_1$ we have

$$p_1 = p_1' \cos\theta + p_2' \cos\phi \qquad\qquad ...(37b)$$

$$0 = p_1' \sin\theta - p_2' \sin\phi \qquad \qquad ...(37c)$$

Furthermore if the collision is elastic viz. the asymptotive initial and final kinetic energies (when the particles are far away from each other) are the same by conservation of energy

$$\frac{p_1^2}{2m_1} = \frac{p_1'^2}{2m_1} + \frac{p_2'^2}{2m_2} \qquad \qquad ...(37d)$$

with three equations, given the incident energy (or momentum) and the masses m_1 and m_2 we have four unknowns $(p_1', p_2', \theta, \phi)$ and three equations so we need one more piece of data. For a given angle θ of scattering we can find the final momentums p_1', p_2' and the angle ϕ of recoil of the target particle.

Note, however that for the special case where $m_1 = m_2$ equation (37d) reduces to

$$p_1^2 = p_1'^2 + p_2'^2$$

which implies that $\vec{p}_1'$ and $\vec{p}_2'$ form two sides of a right angled triangle with $\vec{p}_1$ as the hypotenuse by virtue of Pythagoras' Theorem. Thus the two final momentum $\vec{p}_1'$ and $\vec{p}_2'$ are at right angle to each other.

Note that (37b) and (37c) may be writen as $p_2' \cos\phi = p_1 - p_1' \cos\theta$ and $p_2' \sin\phi = +p_1' \sin\theta$ which when squared and added gives $p_2'^2 = p_1^2 + p_1'^2 - 2p_1 p_1' \cos\theta$ which when substituted into the energy conservation equation (37d) enable us to calculate p_1'/p_1 that is the ratio of the magnitude of the final and initial projectile momenta, in terms of the masses and $\cos\theta$ yielding from the quadratic equation.

$$\frac{p_1'}{p_1} = \frac{m_1}{m_1+m_2} \cos\theta \pm \sqrt{\left(\frac{m_1}{m_1+m_2}\right)^2 \cos^2\theta + \frac{m_2-m_1}{m_1+m_2}} \qquad ...(38)$$

If $m_1 > m_2$ viz. projectile heavier than the stationary target then there is a minimum value of $\cos^2\theta$ or a maximum angle θ of scattering otherwise the quantity under the radical shall be negative and p_1'/p_1 will become complex and hence unphysical. The algebra is easily worked out to give

$$\cos^2\theta_{max} = 1 - \frac{m_2^2}{m_1^2} \qquad ...(39)$$

Thus θ can range from zero (target missed!) to the maximum value given by the above which is less then $\pi/2$. If $m_2 > m_1$, then all values of θ from 0 to π are allowed.

If $\theta = 0$ or π the problem becomes essentially one dimensional. You have

$$\frac{p_1'}{p_1} = \frac{m_1}{m_1+m_2} \pm \frac{m_2}{m_1+m_2}$$

Thus, with the positive sign $p_1' = p_1$ (corresponding to a miss) or $\dfrac{p_1'}{p_1} = \dfrac{m_1 - m_2}{m_1 + m_2}$ a head on collision.

For the case $m_1 = m_2$ you miss when $\theta = 0$ and $\dfrac{p_1'}{p_1} = 1$ or you have a head on collision when $p_1' = 0$. That is the projectile after collision remains at rest and the target particle comes off with all the kinetic energy.

Bodies with internal structure as distinct from point particles could absorb or release energy on collision. Thus for example a target particle could comprise of two masses attached to each other by a relaxed spring. The projectile could collide with this target and thereby compress the spring so that some of the kinetic energy of the projectile could go into the internal excitation of the target. Such a collision would be called **endoergic** that is some of the kinetic energy of translational motion of the projectile is absorbed in the internal excitation of the composite target. If Q is the energy expended or spent in exciting the target then the conservation of total energy would dictate that

$$T_1 = T_1' + T_2' + Q \qquad \qquad ...(40)$$

where T_1, T_1' and T_2' are the kinetic energy of the incident projectile, the full projectile and the recoiling target respectively as some of the incident energy (Q) has gone into producing internal excitation of the target. We may equally well imagine a situation where the collision could be instrumental in releasing some energy such as the contact with projectile actuating an explosion which released chemical energy into mechanical energy. Such a situation would correspond to an exoergic inelastic collision. Thus using momentum conservation and the modified form of energy conservation (involving the possibility of internal excitation of the target particle etc.) expressed in equation (40) with the sign and magnitude of Q determined as per the details of the problem we may relate kinematically the initial and the final states of the collision.

As an extreme example of such inelastic collisions consider such a complete encounter in which a projectile (a bullet for example) of mass m_1 and velocity $\vec{v}_1$ strike and embedded itself into an object of mass m_2 initially at rest. Let the velocity of the two together after the collision be $\vec{v}'$. The conservation of momentum dictates that $\vec{v}'$ must be in the same direction as $\vec{v}_1$ and we must have

$$m_1 \vec{v}_1 = (m_1 + m_2)\vec{v}'$$

Thus the velocities of the composite after collision is

$$\vec{v}' = \frac{m_1}{m_1 + m_2}\vec{v}_1$$

Clearly the kinetic energy of the bodies in such a collision is not conserved. An amount of energy discernable as the tangible initial and final kinetic energies is converted into internal degrees of freedom in the form of heat and this is given by

$$Q = \frac{1}{2}m_1 v_1^2 - \frac{1}{2}(m_1 + m_2)v'^2 = \frac{1}{2}m_1 v_1^2 \left(\frac{m_2}{m_1 + m_2} \right)$$

Section 7. THE TWO BODY PROBLEM

In section 3 we have already explained how the problem of two bodies moving under their mutual gravitational froce can be reduced to the problem of a single "particle" with a reduced mass moving in the influence of the force $\vec{F}$ satisfying the equation

$$m\frac{d^2\vec{r}}{dt^2} = \vec{F}$$

where $\vec{r}$ is the relative separation.

Furthermore we showed that if $\vec{F}$ is a central force viz. $\vec{F} = F\hat{r}$ where $F = |\vec{F}|$ the magnitude of the force, then, (by virtue of section 4) equation (12) the angular momentum $\vec{L} = \vec{r} \times \vec{p}$ is conserved. Since $\vec{L}$ being the cross or vector product of $\vec{r}$ and $\vec{p}$ must be perpendicular to both the vectors $\vec{r}$ and $\vec{p}$ and since $\vec{L}$ is constant for a central force therefore its direction and magnitude are both fixed and thus $\vec{r}$ and $\vec{p}$ must both lie in a plane at right angle to the fixed $\vec{L}$. Choosing $\vec{L}$ to be along the Z-axis the vectors $\vec{r}$ and $\vec{p}$ shall both lie in the XY-plane. In the case of central forces to determine the solutions of the Newton's equations and hence the orbits it is convenient to use polar coordinates rather than the cartesian in the plane of motion. So we have

$$x = r\cos\theta \quad y = r\sin\theta \qquad \ldots(41a)$$

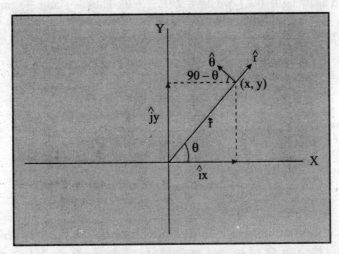

Fig. 6

The notation is shown in Fig. 6 where

$$\vec{r} = \hat{i}x + \hat{j}y \quad \text{and} \quad r = \sqrt{x^2 + y^2}, \ \theta = \tan^{-1}\left(\frac{y}{x}\right) \qquad \ldots(41b)$$

The vectors $\hat{r}$ and $\hat{\theta}$ are unit vectors in the directions of increasing r and θ respectively [just as $\hat{i}$ and $\hat{j}$ were those along the X and Y axes], Note, however, that while $\hat{i}$ and $\hat{j}$ were fixed unit vectors along X and along Y wherever you are, the unit vectors $\hat{r}$ and $\hat{\theta}$ depend on where you are. Indeed the unit vector $\hat{r}$ making an angle θ with the X-axis would have components $\cos\theta$ along X and $\sin\theta$ along Y and hence we have

$$\hat{r} = \cos\theta\hat{i} + \sin\theta\hat{j} \qquad ...(41c)$$

On the other hand the unit vector $\hat{\theta}$ (see Fig. 6) has a component along X which is $-\cos(90° - \theta) = -\sin\theta$ and along Y its component is $\cos\theta$ and thus

$$\hat{\theta} = -\sin\theta\hat{i} + \cos\theta\hat{j} \qquad ...(41d)$$

Note that $\dfrac{d\hat{r}}{d\theta} = -\sin\theta\hat{i} + \cos\theta\hat{j} = \hat{\theta}$ which we record as

$$\frac{d\hat{r}}{d\theta} = \hat{\theta} \qquad ...(41e)$$

and the

$$\frac{d\hat{\theta}}{d\theta} = -\cos\theta\hat{i} - \sin\theta\hat{j} = -\hat{r} \qquad ...(41f)$$

Equations (41e) and (41f) are kind of natural as $\hat{r}\cdot\hat{r} = 1$ and thus $2\hat{r}\cdot\dfrac{d\hat{r}}{d\theta} = 0$ (differentiating with respect to θ) and again as $\hat{\theta}\cdot\hat{\theta} = 1$ we have $2\hat{\theta}\cdot\dfrac{d\hat{\theta}}{d\theta} = 0$. Thus $\dfrac{d\hat{r}}{d\theta}$ and $\dfrac{d\hat{\theta}}{d\theta}$ must be perpendicular to $\hat{r}$ and $\hat{\theta}$ respectively.

$$\vec{r} = r\hat{r}$$
$$\frac{d\vec{r}}{dt} = \dot{r}\hat{r} + r\frac{d}{dt}\hat{r}$$
$$= \dot{r}\hat{r} + r\left(\frac{d}{d\theta}\hat{r}\right)\frac{d\theta}{dt}$$
$$= \dot{r}\hat{r} + r\dot{\theta}\hat{\theta} \qquad ...(41g)$$
$$\frac{d^2\vec{r}}{dt^2} = (\ddot{r} - r\dot{\theta}^2)\hat{r} + (r\ddot{\theta} + 2\dot{r}\dot{\theta})\hat{\theta} \qquad ...(41h)$$

After these necessary preliminaries let us concentrate on our solar system and that too on a particular planet P and the sun $\odot$ of masses m_P and M_S respectively. As $M_S \gg m_P$ the reduced mass

$$m = \frac{m_P M_S}{m_P + M_S} = \frac{m_P}{1 + \dfrac{m_P}{m_S}} \approx m_P.$$ The force determining the motion of the planet is governed mainly by

the sun; the other planets and satellites exerting some perturbations which may at first be neglected.

Thus the force exerted by the sun on the planet P is $\vec{F} = -\dfrac{Gm_P M_S}{r^2}\hat{r}$ where r is the relative separation of the two and as $m_P \simeq m$, the reduced mass, the Newton's equation of motion introducing $GM_S \equiv \gamma$, becomes

$$\frac{d^2\vec{r}}{dt^2} = -\frac{GM_S}{r^2}\hat{r} \equiv \frac{-\gamma}{r^2}\hat{r} \qquad \qquad \text{...(42)}$$

Note here that to this very good approximation $m_P \simeq m$ all the planets obey equation (42). We proceed to solve equation (42) using plane polar coordinates.

Using equations (41g) and (41h) we have

$$\ddot{r} - r\dot{\theta}^2 = -\frac{\gamma}{r^2} \qquad \qquad \text{...(43a)}$$

$$r\ddot{\theta} + 2\dot{r}\dot{\theta} = 0 \qquad \qquad \text{...(43b)}$$

Multiplying (43b) by mr we obtain

$$mr^2\ddot{\theta} + 2mr\dot{r}\dot{\theta} = 0$$

which can be written as

$$\frac{d}{dt}(mr^2\dot{\theta}) = 0 \qquad \qquad \text{...(44)}$$

But
$$\vec{L} = \vec{r} \times \vec{p} = \vec{r} \times m\dot{\vec{r}} = m\vec{r} \times (\dot{r}\hat{r} + r\dot{\theta}\hat{\theta})$$

$$= mr^2\dot{\theta}\hat{k}$$

as $\vec{r} \times \hat{r} = 0$ and $\vec{r} \times \hat{\theta} = r\hat{k}$ where $\hat{k}$ is the unit vector along z-axis.

Thus equation (44) stands for the conservation of the magnitude of the angular momentum.

Accordingly, we have

$$mr^2\dot{\theta} = L \qquad \qquad \text{...(45a)}$$

thus the solution of equation (44) which when inserted into equation (43a) gives us

$$\ddot{r} - \frac{L^2}{m^2 r^3} = -\frac{\gamma}{r^2} \qquad \qquad \text{...(45b)}$$

multiplying by m and transposing the term contains L^2 to the right, we have

$$m\ddot{r} = \frac{-m\gamma}{r^2} + \frac{L^2}{mr^3} \qquad \qquad \text{...(46)}$$

This equation (46) has the form of an equation of motion in one dimension (in the radial coordinate) for a particle of mass m moving under the influence of the radial gravitational force and an additional repulsive "centrifugal force" $\dfrac{L^2}{mr^3}$. Actually L^2/mr^3 is not a force because in fact it arose from the term containing mass times acceleration in the Newton's equation. We may infact go on to introduce the 'effective potential' energy through

$$V_{eff}(r) = -\int\left(-\frac{m\gamma}{r^2} + \frac{L^2}{mr^3}\right)dr = -\frac{m\gamma}{r} + \frac{L^2}{2mr^2}$$

choosing the constant of integration to be zero corresponding to the vanishing of V_{eff} as $r \to \infty$ (far away from the source of the gravitational attraction). The second term $\dfrac{L^2}{2mr^2}$ often called the centrifugal potential is actually not a true potential but in fact comes from the angular part of the kinetic energy. It is a "pseudo potential".

Multiplying equation (46) by $\dot{r}$ and integrating with respect to time

$$\frac{1}{2}m\dot{r}^2 + \int\left(\frac{\gamma m}{r^2} - \frac{L^2}{mr^3}\right)dr = \text{constant}$$

which yields

$$\frac{1}{2}m\dot{r}^2 + \frac{L^2}{2mr^2} - \frac{\gamma m}{r} = E \qquad \ldots(47)$$

That is we have recognised the constant of integration as the total energy (kinetic + potential) which is a constant. Thus the Newton's equation of motion which is a second order differential equation for $\bar{r}$ has been integrated once and what remains is to write

$$\frac{dr}{dt} = \pm\sqrt{\frac{2}{m}}\sqrt{E - \frac{L^2}{2mr^2} + \frac{\gamma m}{r}} \qquad \ldots(48a)$$

and hence as

$$dt = \sqrt{\frac{m}{2}}\frac{1}{\sqrt{E - \dfrac{L^2}{2mr^2} + \dfrac{\gamma m}{r}}}\,dr$$

we have

$$t = \pm\sqrt{\frac{m}{2}}\int dr\,\frac{1}{\sqrt{E - \dfrac{L^2}{2mr^2} + \dfrac{\gamma m}{r}}} + t_0 \qquad \ldots(48b)$$

where t_0 is some initial times and the plus and minus signs before the integral tells us in which direction the initial radial velocity started off. The above tells us how r varies with t.

To determine the orbit $r(\theta)$ using (48a) in conjunction with equation (45a) which gives $\dfrac{d\theta}{dt} = \dfrac{L}{mr^2}$ we have

$$\frac{dr}{d\theta} = \sqrt{\frac{2}{m}} \sqrt{E - \frac{L^2}{2mr^2} + \frac{\gamma m}{r}} \frac{mr^2}{L} \qquad ...(49a)$$

where

$$\theta = \frac{L}{\sqrt{2m}} \int \frac{dr}{r^2} \frac{1}{\sqrt{E - \frac{L^2}{2mr^2} + \frac{\gamma m^2}{r}}} dr + \theta_0 \qquad ...(49b)$$

To perform the integral put $\frac{1}{r} = u$ or $-\frac{1}{r^2} dr = du$ and thus the integral becomes

$$-\frac{L}{\sqrt{2m}} \int du \frac{1}{\sqrt{E - \frac{L}{2m} u^2 + \gamma m u}} = -\frac{L}{\sqrt{2m}} \cos^{-1} \frac{\left(1 - \frac{uL^2}{m^2\gamma}\right)}{\sqrt{1 + \frac{2EL^2}{m^3\gamma^2}}}$$

or after solving for u by inserting this in equation (49b), we obtain

$$\frac{1}{r} = \frac{m^2\gamma}{L^2}\left[1 - \sqrt{1 + \frac{2EL^2}{m^3r^2}} \cos(\theta - \theta_0)\right] \qquad ...(50)$$

which is the equation for a conic section in plane polar coordinates $\frac{l}{r} = 1 - \varepsilon \cos(\theta - \theta_0)$, l being the latus rectum and ε the eccentricity, the initial θ_0 determining its orientation. If E < 0 then ε < 1 and we have the equation for an ellipse.

An ellipse is defined as a curve traced out by a particle moving such that the sum of its distances from two fixed points F and F' (called the focii of the ellipse) is a fixed constant.

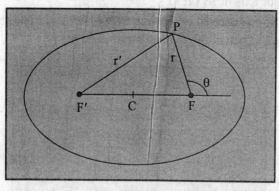

Fig. 7

viz. $r + r' = 2a \equiv$ major axis of the ellipse. The distance $CF = a\varepsilon$ where ε is known as the eccentricity of the ellipse ($\varepsilon \to 0$ F and F' tend to C and the ellipse becomes a circle). The distance between the focii is clearly $2a\varepsilon$. Focussing attention on the $\Delta(PF'F)$ we have the cosine law of triangles

$r'^2 = r^2 + (2a\varepsilon)^2 + 4a\varepsilon r \cos\theta$ and as $r' = r - 2a$ we obtain after some simplification the equation for an ellipse in plane polar coordinates with the origin at one of the focii, namely

$$r = \frac{a(1-\varepsilon^2)}{1+\varepsilon\cos\theta} \qquad \qquad ...(51)$$

with $0 < \varepsilon < 1$. It is readily seen that equation (50) is nothing but equation (51) with $\theta_0 = 0$ which being merely a tilt of the major axis. The minor axis of the ellipse intersects it at two points on it where $r = r' = a$ as can be seen from the figure from which it is easy to derive that the semi major axis $b = a\sqrt{1-\varepsilon^2}$. The area of the ellipse is $\pi ab = \pi a^2 \sqrt{1-\varepsilon^2}$. Furthermore, just as the ellipse is described by equation (51), the other conic sections can also be written very conveniently in the plane polar coordinate system. Thus the parabola is described by

$$r = \frac{a}{1+\cos\theta} \qquad \qquad ...(52)$$

and the hyperbola by

$$r = \frac{a(\varepsilon^2 - 1)}{1-\varepsilon\cos\theta} \text{ with } \varepsilon > 1 \qquad \qquad ...(53)$$

Newton was able to understand on the basis of his Laws of Motion and his hypothesis of the Universal Law of Gravitational attraction, the earlier empirical laws of the motion of planets around the sun in the solar system, which were announced by Johannes Kepler (early in the seventeenth century) on the basis of detailed observations made by Tycho Brahe on the motion of the planets. These were:

1. The orbit of each planet is in a plane and describes an ellipse with the sun at one of its focii.
2. Areas swept out by the radius vector from the sun to a planet in equal times are equal.
3. The square of the period of revolution of a planet around the sun is proportional to the cube of the semi-major axis of its orbit.

The first law of Kepler was derived by Newton from basic laws of mechanics as per equation (50) for $E < 0$ which correspond to bound orbits like that of planets.

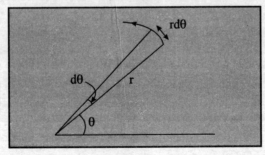

Fig. 8

The second law of Kepler is simply a consequence of the fact that the gravitational force being central orbital angular momentum is a constant [see equation 45(a)] and as $mr^2\dot{\theta} = L = $ constant, we note that, the area subtended by two radius vectors $\vec{r}$ and $\vec{r} + d\vec{r}$ at angles θ and $\theta + d\theta$ is $\frac{1}{2}(rd\theta)r$ and if the time taken to move from one point on the orbit to the other so displaced is dt then the area swept out per unit time is nothing but $\frac{1}{2}r^2\frac{d\theta}{dt}$ which is a constant given by $\frac{L}{2m}$.

The third law of Kepler simply follows from the fact that the area of the ellipse is $\pi ab = \pi a^2(1-\varepsilon^2)^{1/2}$ and since $\varepsilon = \sqrt{1+\frac{2EL^2}{m^2r^2}}$ and $a = \frac{L^2}{m^2r^2}$ we have the area of the ellipse divided by the aerial velocity which is nothing but the period τ of the planet resulting in

$$\tau^2 = ma^3$$

For $E > 0$ and $E = 0$ we have hyperbolic or parabolic orbits. These are of interest for the case of comets.

An alternative route to arrive at the Keplerian orbit from Newton's equation of motion stems from equations (45a) and (45b), the former through $mr^2\dot{\theta} = L$ (conservation of angular momentum) enables us to write $\frac{d}{dt} = \frac{L}{mr^2}\frac{d}{d\theta}$, while the latter for the radial acceleration $\ddot{r} = -\frac{\gamma}{r^2} + \frac{L^2}{m^2r^3}$ can lead us to a differential equation for the angular dependence of r by writing $\frac{d^2}{dt^2} = \frac{L}{mr^2}\frac{d}{d\theta}\frac{L}{mr^2}\frac{d}{d\theta}$. A vast simplification takes place if we make the substitution $\frac{1}{r} = u$, for then $\frac{d^2r}{dt^2}$ becomes $\frac{Lu^2}{m}\frac{d}{d\theta}\frac{Lu^2}{m}\frac{d}{d\theta}\left(\frac{1}{u}\right)$ $= -\frac{L^2}{m^2}u^2\frac{d^2u}{d\theta^2}$ and accordingly equation [45(b)] simplifies to $-\frac{L^2}{m^2}u^2\frac{d^2u}{d\theta^2} = -\gamma u^2 + \frac{L^2}{m^2}u^3$ and even more dramatically

$$\frac{d^2u}{d\theta^2} = -u + \frac{m^2\gamma}{L^2}$$

the solution of which is easily seen to be

$$u = A\cos(\theta - \theta_0) + \frac{m^2\gamma}{L^2}$$

where A and θ_0 are constants to be fixed using the initial conditions. With $u = \frac{1}{r}$ it becomes clear that we have the general equation for a conic section in polar coordinates. We may choose $\theta_0 = 0$ which is merely choosing the X-axis of the coordinate system along the axis of the conic section. Thus we have $u = \frac{m^2\gamma}{L^2} + A\cos\theta$. It remains to fix the constant A, which can be achieved through the energy expression equation (47) $\frac{1}{2}m\dot{r}^2 + \frac{L^2}{2mr^2} - \frac{\gamma m}{r} = E = \frac{L^2}{2m}\left[\left(\frac{du}{d\theta}\right)^2 + u^2\right] - \gamma mu$ re-expressed in terms of u which

gives when substituting the solution for u $A^2 = \frac{2mE}{L^2} + \frac{m^4\gamma^2}{L^4}$, so that the orbit equation expressing r as

a function of θ stands completely determined in terms of the energy E and the angular momentum L:

$$\frac{L^2/(m\gamma)}{r} = 1 + \sqrt{1 + \frac{2EL^2}{m^2\gamma^2}}\cos\theta$$

which is in the standard form for the conic section with $L^2/(m\gamma) \equiv l$, the latus-rectum, and the radical

$\sqrt{1 + \frac{2EL^2}{m^2\gamma^2}} = \varepsilon$ the eccentricity. For bound orbits $E = -|E| < 0$ we have the eccentricity $\varepsilon < 1$ and we

have elliptic orbits of the planets. The special case when $E = -\frac{m^2\gamma^2}{2L^2}$ we have $\varepsilon = 0$ and what results

is a circular orbit of radius $r = L^2/(m\gamma)$. For the case $E = 0$ the orbit is parabolic and for $E > 0$ we have

$\varepsilon > 1$ and the orbits are hyperbolic and correspond to comets that never return.

□□□

2 The Lagrangian and Hamiltonian Formalisms

Section 1. MOTIVATION

The Newtonian approach to mechanics is based on the force-momentum approach and is hence vectorial in nature as both force and momenta have magnitude as well as direction. The Lagrangian (and Hamiltonian) approach on the other hand are based on scalar functions. While no doubt for simple systems the directional properties (of vectors) are readily imagined and do indeed aid our intuition but when the system gets complicated the Lagrangian method as we shall see gives a mathematically simpler approach.

Furthermore in the Newtonian approach even for a simple system as that of a particle constrained to lie on a horizontal table but subjected to other forces one has to take into account the force of reaction of the table on the particles which balances the force of gravity on the particle. Thus internal forces (such as the force of tension keeping the length of a string fixed, joints, contacts and other constraining forces) have to be included in the Newtonian description. In the Lagrangian formalism, however, as we shall see, only active forces shall be of significance and forces of constraint shall not appear explicitly. The Lagrangian method is thus more attractive for complicated systems. If, however, we need to look at the forces of constant (such as tensions on strings) needed for the design of machinery then we shall see how the Lagrange multiplier method can furnish us with these as well.

The introduction of generalized coordinates which marks the very start of the Lagrange method makes the approach applicable to a wide variety of systems (e.g. electrical circuit and the theory of fields etc.) and enables us to deal with independent coordinates describing a system in a mathematically simpler manner.

However, the Lagrangian method as it stands in its primitive form is confined to conservation systems and if one has velocity dependent forces etc. the Newtonian approach is more direct. In essence therefore both the formalisms have advantages and disadvantages and the students should best be familiar with both.

Section 2. GENERALISED COORDINATES AND CONSTRAINTS

With a system of N particles moving in three dimensions interacting with each other and their motions governed by Newton's Law of Motion, but otherwise free from constraints we require a total of $3N$ coordinates $x^{(1)}, y^{(1)}, z^{(1)}, x^{(2)}, y^{(2)}, z^{(2)}; \ldots x^{(N)}, y^{(N)}, z^{(N)}$ to describe the configuration of the system at any given time t. The coordinates we use may not be Cartesian and indeed for notational and conceptual convenience we shall designate these as $x_1, x_2, \ldots, x_k, \ldots x_{3N}$ viz. x_k ($k = 1, \ldots 3N$). The system may however be subjected to constraints (say C in number) so that the number of independent coordinates needed to describe the system are then $3N - C = f$ and we may then assert that we have a system with $f = 3N - C$ degrees of freedom (viz. the number of independent coordinates needed are then f in number say $q_1, q_2, \ldots q_f$). These new variables are then termed to constitute a proper set of generalized coordinates.

Consider for the sake of illustration a single particle moving freely in three dimensions. We need three coordinates x, y, z to describe this particle. However, suppose that this particle is constrained to move on a fixed circular loop of radius a say.

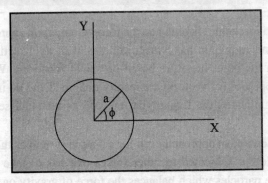

Fig. 1

Choosing the fixed plane of the circle to be the XY plane and the fact that the particle must confine itself through forces of constraint (say that forcing a bead threaded through a circular wire loop to confine its motion along the wire) to lie on the circle we have two equations of constraint

$$z = 0$$

$$x^2 + y^2 = a^2$$

Thus the number of degrees of freedom for the system is just $f = 3 - 2 = 1$. The generalised coordinate in the case is best chosen to be the angle ϕ as shown in the figure.

Another example would be far instance a rigid body made up out of N particles with $N \geq 3$. Here the $3N$ degrees of freedom of N particles in 3 dimensions would be constrained by the $\dfrac{N(N-1)}{2}$ distances between each pair of particles being fixed thereby making up a rigid body. Carefully accounting for the constraints one would ultimately have only six independent coordinates – three to describe the location of the centre of mass of the system and three to describe the orientation of the body.

Constraints that can be specified in the form of equations relating the coordinates are called **holonomic**. Constraints can sometimes be specified on the velocities. An example would be a disc of radius ρ which rolls without slipping down an inclined plane. Here using the notation depicted in Fig. 2 with s the distance down the incline $\dfrac{ds}{dt} = \rho \dfrac{d\phi}{dt}$ but this implies that $ds = \rho d\phi$ and hence $s - \rho\phi = $ constant. So again the constraint is holonomic because here we could integrate the equation of constraint. However it may happen that the equation for constraints in terms of derivatives is not

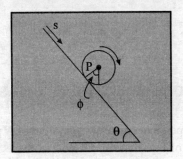

Fig. 2

integrable. In such a situation we would have a non-holonomic constraints. We shall however not deal with such systems but shall confine our attention to holonomic constraints only.

Of course the equations of constraint could very well be time dependent. Thus in the case of the particle sliding along the circular loop but the wire itself rotating with an angular velocity ω, say, along the vertical diameter, we have a time-dependent constraint.

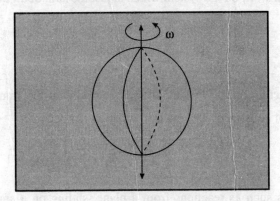

Fig. 3

A sceleronomic constraints is one that is independent of time; a rheonomic constraint contains time explicitly.

Thus in general with holonomic constraints one could use the equation of constraint to define $f = 3N - C$ independent coordinates $q_k = (k = 1, \ldots f)$ and accordingly one could also write the $3N$ Cartesian coordinates in terms of the generalized constraints

$$x_l = x_l(q_1, \ldots \ldots q_f, t) \qquad \ldots(1)$$

with
$$l = 1, \ldots 3N$$

Also using the fundamental rule for partial differentiation, an infinitesimal change in the cartesian coordinates may be written as

$$dx_l = \frac{\partial x_l}{\partial q_1} dq_1 + \ldots + \frac{\partial x_l}{\partial q_f} dq_f + \frac{\partial x_l}{\partial t} dt$$

$$= \sum_{k=1}^{f} \frac{\partial x_l}{\partial q_k} dq_k + \frac{\partial x_l}{\partial t} dt \qquad \qquad \qquad \text{...(2)}$$

Section 3. THE PRINCIPLE OF VIRTUAL WORK AND STATICS

Consider a sceleronomic (time independent constraints) system of N particles located at $\vec{r}_1, \vec{r}_2 \ldots \ldots \vec{r}_N$ in a time independent static scenario of equilibrium. Of course these would remain in that very state if and only if the **net** force on each of the particles is zero and the system is in equilibrium or $\vec{F}_l = 0$, $l = 1, \ldots, N$. To study such systems and the forces internal and external it is useful to **imagine** virtual displace $\delta \vec{r}_l$ of the constituent 'particles' which are infinitesimal, take place instantaneously (viz. $dt = 0$ in equation (2) above), and are carried out consistent with the constraints [equation (1)].

Now since at equilibrium the **net** force $\vec{F}_l$ on each particle say the lth must be zero, evidently the work performed by that particle undergoing a virtual displace $\delta \vec{r}_l$ which is $\vec{F}_l \cdot \delta \vec{r}_l$ must be zero and accordingly the total virtual work on the system which is just the sum of all these zeroes can be nothing else but zero and thus

$$\delta W = \sum_{l=1}^{N} \vec{F}_l \cdot \delta \vec{r}_l = 0 \qquad \qquad \qquad \text{...(3)}$$

The total force $\vec{F}_l$ acting on the lth particle may comprise of the sum of an externally applied force $\vec{F}_l^{(ext)}$ and a force of constraint $\vec{f}_l^{(c)}$ so that equation (3) becomes

$$\delta W = \sum_{l=1}^{N} \vec{F}_l^{(ext)} \cdot \delta \vec{r}_l + \sum_{l=1}^{N} \vec{f}_l^{(c)} \cdot \delta \vec{r}_l = 0 \qquad \qquad \qquad \text{...(4)}$$

Non-frictional forces such as reactions from a plane, sliding on a smooth frictionless surface, rolling contact without slipping do no work under a virtual displacement (forces being perpendicular to the virtual displacement) $\vec{f}_l^{(c)} \cdot \delta \vec{r}_l = 0$. Thus in the absence of work done by friction or dissipative forces we have the principle of virtual work

$$\delta W = \sum_{l=1}^{N} \vec{F}_l^{(ext)} \cdot \delta \vec{r}_l = 0 \qquad \qquad \qquad \text{...(5)}$$

Now we cannot equate to zero each term in the sum occurring in equation (5) but if we could replace the $\delta \vec{r}_l$ by δq_k where q_k are the independent generalized coordinates (which take into account the constraints) then this could be done.

Accordingly we use equation (2) but we may set $dt = 0$ as all virtual displacements are considered to be instantaneous.

Thus

$$\delta \vec{r}_l = \sum_{k} \frac{\partial \vec{r}_l}{\partial q_k} \partial q_k \qquad \qquad \qquad \text{...(6)}$$

which when substituted into equation (5) yields

$$\delta W = \sum_{l=1}^{N} \vec{F}_{l}^{(ext)} \cdot \delta \vec{r}_{l} = \sum_{l=1}^{N} \sum_{k=1}^{f} \vec{F}_{l}^{(ext)} \cdot \frac{\partial \vec{r}_{l}}{\partial q_{k}} \delta q_{k}$$

$$\equiv \sum_{k=1}^{f} Q_{k} \delta q_{k} = 0 \qquad \qquad ...(7)$$

where in the last but one step we have introduced the concept of generalised forces

$$Q_{k} = \sum_{l=1}^{N} \vec{F}_{l}^{(ext)} \cdot \frac{\partial \vec{r}_{l}}{\partial q_{k}} \qquad \qquad ...(8)$$

corresponding to the coordinate q_k. Note, however, that Q_k is a scalar and not a vector and also that Q_k need not have the dimension of force (MLT^{-2}) however the product $Q_k q_k$ will always have the dimension of work. Now since δq_k are all arbitrary and independent of each other from equation (7) each term, in the sum over k can be equated to zero and since δq_k is arbitrary the condition for equilibrium becomes.

$$Q_{k} = 0 \text{ for all } k \qquad \qquad ...(9)$$

We cite an example to illustrate the usefulness of this principle.

Consider a straight uniform rod with mass M of length $2L$ (an idealized ladder), reclining against a smooth frictionless vertical wall and with its other end on an horizontal floor making with it an angle θ and tied to the base of the wall with a massless inextensible string as shown in Fig. 4. Find the tension on the string.

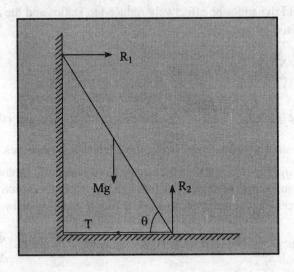

Fig. 4

Take the mid-point (centre-of-gravity) of the rod to be at a height h from the floor and the lower end of the rod at a distance x from the wall. Clearly

$$x = 2L \cos \theta \quad \text{and} \quad h = L \sin \theta \qquad \qquad ...(10)$$

The forces acting on the rod are the weight Mg, downward, the tension due to the string, the forces of reaction R_1 and R_2 from the wall and the floor (the latter two being the forces of constraint). With θ the generalised coordinate the Principle of Virtual Work tells us that the two external forces ($M\vec{g}$ and $\vec{T}$) do the work and the reactions $\vec{R}_1$ and $\vec{R}_2$ do not as the virtual displacements are perpendicular to them and hence from equation (10) $\delta x = -2L\sin\theta\,\delta\theta$ and $\delta h = L\cos\theta\,\delta\theta$ we have $\delta W = (-2LT\sin\theta + LMg\cos\theta)\delta\theta$ the expression in parenthesis being the generalised force. At equilibrium the generalised force is zero and hence

$$T = \frac{1}{2}\,Mg\cot\theta$$

Section 4. D'ALEMBERT'S PRINCIPLE AND THE LAGRANGIAN FORMALISM

It was suggested by Bernoulli and subsequently developed by d'Alembert that the Principle of Virtual Work be generalized so as to bring not only statics but also dynamics under its purview. This was achieved by first taking an apparent simple but conceptually rich step by rewriting the Newton's equation of motion for the kth particle in an N-body system as

$$\vec{F}_k - \frac{d\vec{p}_k}{dt} = 0 \qquad \qquad ...(11)$$

and regarding $-\dfrac{d\vec{p}_k}{dt}$ as a 'force' (an inertial effective force) which on addition to $\vec{F}_k$ produces

'equilibrium'. Thus could dynamics be effectively reduced to statics and the Principle of Virtual Work be extended. Thus in place of equation (3), we have

$$\sum_{k=1}^{N}(\vec{F}_k - \dot{\vec{p}}_k)\cdot\delta\vec{r}_k = 0 \qquad \qquad ...(12)$$

As before we write $\vec{F}_k = \vec{F}_k^{(ext)} + \vec{f}_k^{(c)}$ viz. the sum of externally applied forces $\vec{F}_k^{(ext)}$ and forces of constraint $\vec{f}_k^{(c)}$. We shall now transform from the Cartesian coordinates $\vec{r}_k$ ($l = 1, \ldots N$) to the generalised coordinates q_k ($k = 1, \ldots f$) where the equations of constraint (holonomic) are used to obtain independent variables numbering the degrees of freedom. We shall also strictly confine our attention to situations where the forces of constraint do no work and as a result as before we have

$$\delta W = \sum_{l=1}^{N}\vec{F}_l^{(ext)}\cdot\delta\vec{r}_l = \sum_{k=1}^{f}Q_k\delta q_k \text{ with } Q_k = \sum_{l=1}^{N}\vec{F}_l^{(ext)}\cdot\frac{\partial\vec{r}_l}{\partial q_k} \qquad ...(13)$$

the generalised force. But now unlike the static situation we also have the inertial force term to deal with, namely,

$$\sum_{l=1}^{N}\dot{\vec{p}}_l\cdot\delta\vec{r}_l = \sum_{l=1}^{N}\sum_{k=1}^{f}\dot{\vec{p}}_l\cdot\frac{\partial\vec{r}_l}{\partial q_k}\delta q_k$$

$$= \sum_{k=1}^{f} \delta q_k \sum_{l=1}^{N} m_l \frac{d^2 \vec{r}_l}{dt^2} \cdot \frac{\partial \vec{r}_l}{\partial q_k}$$

where we have used $\quad \dot{\vec{p}}_l = \frac{d}{dt} \vec{p}_l = \frac{d}{dt}\left(m_l \frac{d\vec{r}_l}{dt} \right) = m_l \frac{d^2 \vec{r}_l}{dt^2}$. Thus we have

$$\sum_{l=1}^{N} \dot{\vec{p}}_l \cdot \delta \vec{r}_l = \sum_{k=l}^{f} \delta q_k \sum_{l=1}^{N} m_l \left\{ \frac{d}{dt}\left(\frac{d\vec{r}_l}{dt} \cdot \frac{\partial \vec{r}_l}{\partial q_k} \right) - \frac{d\vec{r}_l}{dt} \cdot \frac{d}{dt}\left(\frac{d\vec{r}_l}{\partial q_k} \right) \right\} \quad ...(14)$$

where in the last step in order to write the coefficients of the independent δq_k as a total time derivative we have introduced the first term in the curly brackets and subtracted the extra terms so introduced. We

now concentrate on the term $m_l \dfrac{d}{dt}\left(\dfrac{d\vec{r}_l}{dt} \cdot \dfrac{\partial \vec{r}_l}{\partial q_k} \right)$ and note vide equation (2) that

$$\dot{\vec{r}}_l = \frac{d\vec{r}_l}{dt} = \sum_{k=1}^{f} \frac{\partial \vec{r}_l}{\partial q_k} \dot{q}_k + \frac{\partial \vec{r}_l}{\partial t} dt$$

where we have simply translated from Cartesian vectors to generalised coordinates.

Note $\dfrac{\partial \dot{\vec{r}}_l}{\partial \dot{q}_k} = \dfrac{\partial \vec{r}_l}{\partial q_k}$ and therefore

$$m_l \frac{d}{dt}\left(\frac{d\vec{r}_l}{dt} \cdot \frac{d\vec{r}_l}{dq_k} \right) = m_l \frac{d}{dt}\left(\frac{d\vec{r}_l}{dt} \cdot \frac{d\dot{\vec{r}}_l}{d\dot{q}_k} \right) = m_l \frac{d}{dt}\left(\dot{\vec{r}}_l \frac{d\dot{\vec{r}}_l}{d\dot{q}_k} \right) = \frac{m_l}{2} \frac{d}{dt} \frac{d}{d\dot{q}_k} (\dot{\vec{r}}_l)^2$$

$$= \frac{d}{dt} \frac{d}{d\dot{q}_k}\left(\frac{1}{2} m_l \dot{\vec{r}}_l^2 \right)$$

We note that the quantity in parenthesis in the last step is the kinetic energy of the lth particle and hence the first term in curly brackets in equation (14) is nothing but

$$\sum_{k=1}^{f} \delta q_k \frac{d}{dt} \frac{d}{d\dot{q}_k} T \quad\quad ...(15)$$

where $T = \dfrac{1}{2} \sum_{l=1}^{N} m_l \dot{\vec{r}}_l^2 = $ Total kinetic energy of the system. We shall henceforth use T for the total kinetic energy. At places T shall stand for tension of a string or a time period but this should be clear from the context.

The remaining term in the curly brackets on the right hand side of the last step of equation (14) now needs to be tackled

$$\sum_{l=1}^{N} m_l \frac{d\vec{r}_l}{dt} \cdot \frac{d}{dt}\left(\frac{\partial \vec{r}_l}{\partial q_k} \right) = \frac{\partial}{\partial q_k} \sum_{l=1}^{N} m_l \frac{1}{2}\left(\frac{d\vec{r}_l}{dt} \right)^2 = \frac{\partial}{\partial q_k} T. \quad\quad ...(16)$$

Putting all the terms together, the generalised forces vide equation (13), the 'inertial forces' yielding (15) and (16) we arrive at the consequence of the *d'* Alembert's principle

$$\sum_{k=1}^{f}\left(\frac{d}{dt}\frac{\partial T}{\partial \dot{q}_k} - \frac{\partial T}{\partial q_k} - Q_k\right)\delta q_k = 0 \qquad \qquad \dots(17)$$

As the generalised coordinates q_k ($k = 1, \dots, f$) are all independent and δq_k are arbitrary virtual displacements consistent with the constraints it follows that its coefficients must be zero, or in other words

$$\frac{d}{dt}\frac{\partial T}{\partial \dot{q}_k} - \frac{\partial T}{\partial q_k} - Q_k = 0 \qquad \qquad \dots(18)$$

and there are f such equations. This equation can be further simplified if the external forces $\vec{F}^{(ext)}$ are conservative viz. we can write $\vec{F}_k^{(ext)} = -\vec{\nabla}_k V$ where V is a potential energy (see equation (20) of Chapter 1) for this

$$Q_k = \sum_{l=1}^{N}\vec{F}_k^{(ext)} \cdot \frac{\partial \vec{r}_l}{\partial q_k} = -\sum_{l=1}^{N}(\vec{\nabla}_l V) \cdot \frac{\partial}{\partial q_k}\vec{r}_l$$

But since

$$-\frac{\partial V}{\partial q_k} = -\sum_{l}(\vec{\nabla}_l V) \cdot \frac{\partial}{\partial q_k}\vec{r}_l$$

we realise that

$$Q_k = -\frac{\partial V}{\partial q_k} \qquad \qquad \dots(19)$$

Thus equation (18) becomes

$$\frac{d}{dt}\left(\frac{\partial T}{\partial \dot{q}_k}\right) - \frac{\partial}{\partial q_k}(T - V) = 0 \text{ for } k = 1, \dots f \qquad \qquad \dots(20)$$

Now if the potential V is a function of position only, and is independent of the generalised velocities we can include V with T in the first term of equation (20) putting

$$\frac{\partial T}{\partial \dot{q}_k} = \frac{\partial (T - V)}{\partial \dot{q}_k} \text{ as } \frac{\partial V}{\partial \dot{q}_k} = 0 \text{ and thus we arrive at the equation}$$

$$\frac{d}{dt}\frac{\partial}{\partial \dot{q}_k}(T - V) - \frac{\partial}{\partial q_k}(T - V) = 0 \qquad k = 1, \dots f \qquad \qquad \dots(21)$$

This equation (21) encourages us to introduce a new function L defined through

$$L(q_k, \dot{q}_k, t) = T(q_i, \dot{q}_k, t) - V(q_i) \qquad \qquad \dots(22)$$

which is called the Lagrangian function of the system, in terms of which the equations of motion become

$$\frac{d}{dt}\left(\frac{\partial L}{\partial \dot{q}_k}\right) = \frac{\partial L}{\partial q_k} \qquad k = 1, \dots f \qquad \dots(23)$$

which are second order differential equations and are known as the Lagrange's equations for a conservative, holonomic dynamic system.

Let us consider a few examples to illustrate what has been acheived so far.

The simple pendulum

Consider a simple planar pendulum composed of a bob (*B*) of mass *m* suspended by a massless inextensible string (*SB*) of fixed length *l*, from a fixed point of suspension (*S*) in the earth's gravitational field. We shall treat the bob as a point located at its centre-of-mass. With *O* the lowest point in the swing of the bob, *SO* is the vertical.

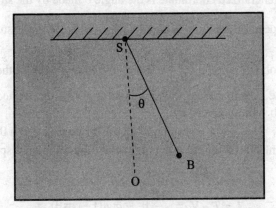

Fig. 5

In the Newtonian approach one considers the 'free-body diagram' for the bob taken as a point particle of mass *m* with the force of gravitation *mg* acting vertically down and the force of tension τ

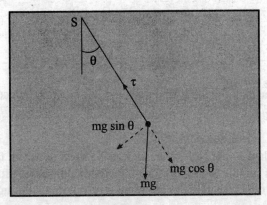

Fig. 6

exerted by the string acting upwards along the string. The component $mg \cos \theta$ of the force of gravity along the string; $mg \cos \theta$ (shown by a dotted line) balances the tension of the string and it is the component $mg \sin \theta$ which is responsible for the motion of the bob along the arc giving the Newton's equation

$$m \frac{d^2}{dt^2} (l\theta) = -mg \sin \theta \simeq -mg \, \theta$$

as $l\theta$ is the length along the arc and in the last step we have made the approximation $\sin \theta \simeq \theta$ valid for small angles of oscillation. This leads to the familiar approximate solution.

$$\theta = \theta_0 = \cos \left\{ \sqrt{g/l} \, (t + \alpha) \right\}$$

In the lagrangian approach one notes that the bob represented by a point particle of mass m moves in three dimensions but by virtue of the fact that the motion is planar it is confined to motion in two dimensions and furthermore since the string by which it is suspended from the fixed point S is inextensible the obvious choice of the generalized coordinate is the angle θ made by the string (suspending the mass m) with the vertical. The speed of the 'bob' is clearly $l\dfrac{d\theta}{dt}$ (where θ is measured in radians) and hence the kinetic energy of the bob is $T = ml^2 \left(\dfrac{d\theta}{dt} \right)^2$. Taking the lowest point of the bob in its motion as the reference level (zero of the potential energy which is arbitrary being defined modulo a constant) the potential energy of the bob will be given by

$$V = mg(l - l \cos \theta) = mgl \, (1 - \cos \theta)$$

as $l - l \cos \theta$ is the height above the lowest point when the angular displacement is θ. Thus the Lagrangian is given by

$$L = T - V = \frac{ml^2}{2} \dot{\theta}^2 - mgl(1 - \cos \theta)$$

where $\dot{\theta} \equiv \dfrac{d\theta}{dt}$. The Lagrange equation of motion

$$\frac{\partial L}{\partial \theta} = \frac{d}{dt} \frac{\partial L}{\partial \left(\dfrac{d\theta}{dt} \right)} = \frac{d}{dt} \frac{\partial L}{\partial \dot{\theta}}$$

because $\dfrac{\partial L}{\partial \theta} = -mgl \sin \theta$ and $\dfrac{\partial L}{\partial \dot{\theta}} = ml^2 \dot{\theta}$ and thus $\dfrac{d}{dt} \left(\dfrac{\partial L}{\partial \dot{\theta}} \right) = ml^2 \ddot{\theta}$ reduces to

$$-mgl \sin \theta = ml^2 \ddot{\theta}$$

which is exactly what we had in the Newtonian approach. Note, however, that here we did not bother with directions and vectors (unlike in the Newtonian method) and also the forces of constraint made no explicit appearance though of course their effect was taken into account through the choice of generalized coordinate θ. Thus ultimately the Lagrangian method, as it must, gives us the same equation of motion as the Newtonian approach.

However from a technological or designer's point of view it is important to know the forces of constraint. For example knowledge about the tension on the string is needed in making a proper choice for a string strong and inextensible enough to serve the purpose. So we use this simple example to illustrate how one determines forces of constraint in the Lagrangian approach. Imagine releasing the constraint by replacing the length l of the string by a variable r. Since we have now made r dynamic we have the Lagrangian

$$L = \frac{1}{2}m\dot{r}^2 + \frac{1}{2}mr^2\dot{\theta}^2 - mgr\cos\theta + \text{constant}$$

the choice of zero of the potential should be fixed and hence the constant. We later impose the constraint $r = l$ to ensure that the pendulum has a fixed length through the equation

$$r = l$$

the variation of which gives the constraint

$$\delta r = 0$$

which we multiply by the Lagrange multiplier λ and accordingly to the virtual work under the displacement δr we add λδr with λ identified with the force of constraint θ_r in the $\hat{r}$ direction. Hence the Lagrange equation which equates to zero the coefficient of the virtual displacement δr becomes

$$\frac{\partial L}{\partial r} - \frac{d}{dt}\frac{\partial L}{\partial \dot{r}} - \lambda = 0 \quad \text{or} \quad m(\ddot{r} - r\dot{\theta}^2) - mg\cos\theta - \lambda = 0$$

and that for the virtual displacement δθ gives

$$\frac{\partial L}{\partial \theta} - \frac{d}{dt}\frac{\partial L}{\partial \dot{\theta}} = 0 \quad \text{or} \quad -mgr\sin\theta - \frac{d}{dt}(mr^2\dot{\theta}) = 0$$

The generalized reaction force λ or Q_r in this case is the negative of the tension τ simply because positive δr (radial virtual displacement) represents an outward displacement.

Hence putting $r = l$ and $\lambda = -\tau$

$$-\lambda = +\tau = ml^2\dot{\theta}^2 + mg\cos\theta$$

$$\ddot{\theta} = -\frac{g}{l}\sin\theta$$

Thus we first solve the equation of motion for θ as before, say in the small angular displacement approximation, and insert the solution in the equation for the force of constraint to determine the tension. Note that the tension on the string is time dependent.

The Atwood machine

Masses m_1 and m_2 are connected by a light (massless in our idealisation) inextensible string of length l passing over a fixed frictionless pulley of radius R. We also assume that the weights move vertically under gravity and force of constraint (no swinging). We clearly have a system with only one degree of freedom. Measuring the gravitational potential energy choosing the zero level at the centre of the pulley and measuring distances downwards as positive we have

Kinetic Energy
$$T = \frac{1}{2}m_1(\dot{x})^2 + \frac{1}{2}m_2\left[\frac{d}{dt}(l - \pi R - x)\right]^2 = \frac{1}{2}m_1\dot{x}^2 + \frac{1}{2}m_2\dot{x}^2$$

Potential Energy
$$V = -m_1gx - m_2g(l - \pi R - x).$$

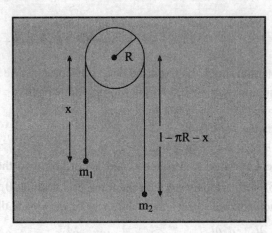

Fig. 7

Thus the Lagrangian

$$L = T - V = \frac{1}{2}(m_1 + m_2)\dot{x}^2 + m_1gx + m_2g(l - \pi R - x)$$

and the Lagrange equation of motion $\dfrac{\partial L}{\partial x} = \dfrac{d}{dt}\dfrac{\partial L}{\partial \dot{x}}$ yields

$$(m_1 - m_2)g = \frac{d}{dt}[(m_1 + m_2)\dot{x}] \implies \ddot{x} = \frac{m_1 - m_2}{m_1 + m_2}g$$

the same as we obtained earlier in the Newtonian approach and this equation is readily solved for x as a function of time:

$$x = x_0 + ut + \frac{1}{2}\frac{m_1 - m_2}{m_1 + m_2}gt^2$$

here $x = x_0$ at $t = 0$, $\dot{x} = u$ at $t = 0$ are the initial conditions.

Now suppose we also wish to find the force of constraint responsible for keeping the total length of the string l a constant (as it is inextensible), namely the tension of the string. To do so we shall temporarily release the constraint (and reimpose it later). As soon as we allow l to stretch the kinetic energy is modified to

$$T = \frac{1}{2}m_1\dot{x}^2 + \frac{1}{2}m_2(\dot{l} - \dot{x})^2$$

To solve for the force of constraint, the tension τ of the string, we allow l to increase by δl, keeping x constant. The virtual work done thereby will be

$$\delta W = (m_2 g - \tau)\delta l = Q_e \, dl$$

where $Q_e = m_2 g - \tau$ is the generalized force corresponding to the "coordinate" l. The Lagrange equation for l becomes

$$\frac{d}{dt}\left(\frac{\partial T}{\partial \dot{l}}\right) - \frac{\partial T}{\partial l} = Q_e = m_2 g - \tau$$

Now $\dfrac{\partial T}{\partial \dot{l}} = m_2(\dot{l} - \dot{x})$ and $\dfrac{d}{dt}\dfrac{\partial T}{\partial \dot{l}} = m_2(\ddot{l} - \ddot{x}) = -m_2\ddot{x}$ since $\dot{l}$ and $\ddot{l}$ should at the end of the day be put equal to zero (the constraint re-imposed). As $\dfrac{\partial T}{\partial l} = 0$, the Lagrange equation in the l 'variable' reduces to

$$-m_2\ddot{x} = m_2 g - \tau$$

and thus

$$\tau = m_2(g + \ddot{x}) = \frac{2m_1 m_2}{m_1 + m_2}g$$

re-inserting $\ddot{x}$ determined earlier. Thus we see that in this case the tension turns out to be independent of time although in general (as the example of the string tension for the pendulum shows) the force of constraint could well change with time.

Section 5. THE HAMILTONIAN FORMALISM

Ignorable coordinates and constants of motion

Given a dynamical system it is very advantageous if one can track down some functions of coordinates and velocities which are constants in time. These are known as constants of the motion. Indeed if in the Lagrangian for a system some generalized coordinate, say q_k, does not appear explicitly then by virtue of Lagrange's equation for that coordinate we have

$$\frac{d}{dt}\left(\frac{\partial L}{\partial \dot{q}_k}\right) = \frac{\partial L}{\partial q_k} = 0$$

and such a q_k is said to be ignorable (but should not be ignored because it leads us immediately to a valuable result):

$$\frac{\partial L}{\partial \dot{q}_k} \equiv p_k = \text{constant of motion as } \frac{d}{dt}p_k = 0$$

Thus $p_k = \dfrac{\partial L}{\partial \dot{q}_k}$, which is called the momentum canonically conjugate to an ignorable coordinate q_k, is a constant of the motion. For instance in the case of motion of a particle moving in a central potential (such as a planet around the sun) the Lagrangian

$$L = \frac{1}{2}mr^2\dot{\theta}^2 + \frac{1}{2}m\dot{r}^2 - V(r)$$

is independent of the angle θ and hence the momentum $p_\theta = \dfrac{\partial L}{\partial \dot{\theta}} = mr^2\dot{\theta}$, which is canonically conjugate to the ignorable coordinate θ, is a constant of the motion. This canonical momentum p_θ is actually the angular momentum of the orbiting particle and indeed its constancy corresponds to the second law of Kepler as $\dfrac{1}{2}r^2\dot{\theta}$ is the areal velocity or the area swept out per second by the line joining the planet to the sun.

As another example if a system of particles is isolated from external forces and only interact amongst themselves the potential energy can only depend on their mutual separation and cannot depend on the coordinates of their centre-of-mass (which depends on the choice of origin which cannot be relevant). Hence the coordinates of the centre-of-mass must be ignorable and therefore the momentum conjugate to the centre-of-mass coordinate which is the momentum of the centre-of-mass or the total momentum of the system must be a constant of motion.

Constancy of the total energy

We know that for an isolated (autonomous) system the total energy, which is the sum of the kinetic and potential energies is a constant. We now go on to show how the Lagrange's equations of motion also lead us to the same conclusion. In a coordinate system that is fixed with respect to time it is clear from the expression for the kinetic energy that the kinetic energy is a quadratic function of the generalised velocities $\dot{q}_k$'s. Therefore, by Euler's Theorem on homogeneous polynomials we may assert that

$$\sum_{i=1}^{f} \dot{q}_k \frac{\partial}{\partial \dot{q}_k} T = 2T.$$

Euler's theorem is intuitively very clear. Consider the most general homogeneous quadratic in two variables x and y, namely $f(x, y) = ax^2 + bxy + cy^2$, where a, b and c are constants. Note that $\left(x\dfrac{\partial}{\partial x} + y\dfrac{\partial}{\partial y}\right)f(x,y) = \left(x\dfrac{\partial}{\partial x} + y\dfrac{\partial}{\partial y}\right)(ax^2 + bxy + cy^2) = 2(ax^2 + bxy + cy^2) = 2f(x,y)$. In exactly the same fashion T being a homogeneous quadratic in $\dot{q}_k$'s we have the above result. Furthermore, if the potential V is independent of the generalised velocities then as $\sum_{i=1}^{f} \dot{q}_k \dfrac{\partial}{\partial \dot{q}_k} V = 0$, we have the result that

$$\sum_{k=1}^{f} \dot{q}_k \frac{\partial}{\partial \dot{q}_k} L = 2T \text{ and as a result}$$

$$\sum_{k=1}^{f} \dot{q}_k \frac{\partial L}{\partial \dot{q}_k} - L = 2T - L = 2T - (T - V) = T + V = E = \text{Total Energy.}$$

We thus are able to connect the Lagrangian with the total energy which is the sum of the kinetic (T) and potential (V) energies.

In order to demonstrate the conservation of energy consider the time derivative of the total energy as depicted in the above equation, allowing temporarily at least for L to be an explicit function of time so that $\dfrac{\partial L}{\partial t} \neq 0$ will be retained as of now. Thus

$$\frac{d}{dt}\left(\sum_{k=1}^{f} \dot{q}_k \frac{\partial L}{\partial \dot{q}_k} - L \right) = \sum_{k=1}^{f}\left(\ddot{q}_k \frac{\partial L}{\partial \dot{q}_k} + \dot{q}_k \frac{d}{dt}\frac{\partial L}{\partial \dot{q}_k} \right) - \sum_{k=1}^{f}\left(\frac{\partial L}{\partial q_k}\dot{q}_k + \frac{\partial L}{\partial \dot{q}_k}\ddot{q}_k + \frac{\partial L}{\partial t} \right)$$

where the first term in the parentheses and brackets on the right hand side arise from the time derivative of the first term in the parentheses on the left hand side and the second term in the summation and the parentheses on the right hand side arise from $\dfrac{dL}{dt}$, as L is a function of q_k, $\dot{q}_k$ and may be explicitly dependent on time t, which would be the case if there were an external explicitly time dependent interaction present (viz. the system was not isolated). Notice that the terms containing $\ddot{q}_k$ cancel. Accordingly we are led, after due cancellation and re-arrangement to

$$\frac{d}{dt}\left(\sum_{k=1}^{f} \dot{q}_k \frac{\partial L}{\partial \dot{q}_k} - L \right) = \sum_{k=1}^{f}\left(\frac{d}{dt}\frac{\partial L}{\partial \dot{q}_k} - \frac{\partial L}{\partial q_k} \right) - \frac{\partial L}{\partial t} = -\frac{\partial L}{\partial t}$$

where in the last step above we have simply used the Lagrange equation of motion to set the term in the summation equal to zero. Thus, in conclusion, if L does not explicitly depend on time $\left(\dfrac{\partial L}{\partial t} = 0 \right)$ we arrive at the result that

$$\sum_{k=1}^{f} \dot{q}_k \frac{\partial L}{\partial \dot{q}_k} - L = E = \text{Total Energy} = \text{Constant}$$

The Hamiltonian's equations of motion

For a conservative holonomic system the dynamics is captured, as we have seen, by the Lagrange's equations of motion

$$\frac{d}{dt}\frac{\partial L}{\partial \dot{q}_k} = \frac{\partial L}{\partial q_k}$$

and we have also seen that it is useful to define the generalised p_k canonically conjugate to the generalised coordinate q_k via

$$p_k = \frac{\partial L}{\partial \dot{q}_k}$$

Furthermore we have seen that if the Lagrangian does not depend explicitly on time $\left(\dfrac{\partial L}{\partial t} = 0 \right.$

then $\displaystyle\sum_{k=1}^{f} \dot{q}_k \dfrac{\partial L}{\partial \dot{q}_k} - L$ or $\displaystyle\sum_{k=1}^{f} p_k \dot{q}_k - L$ is time independent. Therefore it is convenient to take a step

forward to define the Hamiltonian (named after William Rowan Hamilton who first took that step)

$$H = \sum_{k=1}^{f} p_k \dot{q}_k - L$$

As already established if the Lagrangian does not depend explicitly on time and the potential is velocity independent than the Hamiltonian is a constant of the motion and the Hamiltonian function physically represents the total energy of the system.

While the Lagrangian formalism is based on the Lagrangian which is a function of generalized coordinates and generalised velocities (q_k and $\dot{q}_k$) the Hamiltonian method is grounded on generalised

coordinates q_k and their canonically conjugate momenta $p_k = \dfrac{\partial L}{\partial \dot{q}_k}$.

The equations of motion in this picture may be found by considering the variation of H with respect to the variables q_k and p_k. The relation $H = -L + \Sigma p_k \dot{q}_k$ relating the Hamiltonian with the Lagrangian will be used for this purpose. Thus

$$\frac{\partial H}{\partial q_k} = -\frac{\partial L}{\partial q_k} = -\frac{d}{dt}\frac{\partial L}{\partial \dot{q}_k} = -\frac{d}{dt}p_k = -\dot{p}_k$$

where in the first step we have used the fact that the term $\Sigma p_k \dot{q}_k$ in the definition of the Hamiltonian is independent of q_k's, in the second step we use the Lagrange equation of motion and in the third the definition of the momentum conjugate to q_k. Again

$$\frac{\partial H}{\partial p_k} = \frac{\partial}{\partial p_k}[-L + \Sigma p_k \dot{q}_k] = \dot{q}_k$$

Thus the f second order Lagrange equations are replaced in the Hamiltonian formalism by $2f$ first order equations:

$$\dot{q}_k = \frac{\partial H}{\partial p_k}$$

$$\dot{p}_k = -\frac{\partial H}{\partial q_k}$$

$k = 1, \ldots f$.

The Newtonian, Lagrangian and the Hamiltonian formalisms of classical mechanics, it must be emphasised, are essentially equivalent, each with its own advantages, as described at the very outset of this chapter. To these remarks one must add that the Hamiltonian formalism proves to be essential, as we shall see in the next semester (Modern Physics), in the very foundation of Quantum Mechanics which is needed to describe correctly the mechanics of microsystems such as atoms, nuclei and elementary particles.

It may be appropriate to close by taking the simplest of systems the simple harmonic oscillator in one dimension and write down the mathematical description in the three pictures:

Newtonian
$$m\frac{d^2x}{dt^2} = -kx$$

Lagrangian
$$L = \frac{1}{2}m\dot{x}^2 - \frac{1}{2}kx^2$$

$$\frac{\partial L}{\partial x} = \frac{d}{dt}\frac{\partial L}{\partial \dot{x}} \quad \Rightarrow \quad -kx = \frac{d}{dt}m\dot{x} \quad \Rightarrow \quad m\ddot{x} = -kx$$

Hamiltonian
$$p = \frac{\partial L}{\partial \dot{x}} = m\dot{x}$$

$$H = -L + p\dot{x} = -\frac{1}{2}m\dot{x}^2 + \frac{1}{2}kx^2 + p\dot{x}$$

$$= \frac{p^2}{2m} + \frac{1}{2}kx^2$$

$$\dot{x} = \frac{\partial H}{\partial p} = \frac{p}{m}$$

$$\dot{p} = -\frac{\partial H}{\partial x} = -kx$$

Hamilton's principle of least action

We have derived the Lagrange's Equations of Motion from Newton's Laws of Motion (for conservative systems) using the d'Alembert's Principle of Virtual Work. This approach could well be described as the differential point of view. An alternative elegant method was proposed by William Rowan Hamilton, best specified as a functional integral route, known as the principle of Least Action. This manner of thinking has its roots in the Fermat's Principle of Least Time in Optics, according to which; A ray of light in travelling from an initial point to a final point takes the path along which the time taken is an extremum (generally a minimum).

To avoid unnecessary complications we shall begin with a system with a single degree of freedom and hence described by a single generalised coordinate q. This will later be generalised in a simple and obvious manner to systems with several degrees of freedom described by $\{q_k\}$. The Hamilton's Principle begins by defining what is called the action integral

$$S = \int_{t_i}^{t_f} L[q(t), \dot{q}(t), t]dt$$

where L is the Lagrangian and $q(t)$ is any path starting at some fixed $q(t_i)$ at an initial time t_i and ending up at $q(t_f)$ at the final time t_f. In the figure below several such paths are shown.

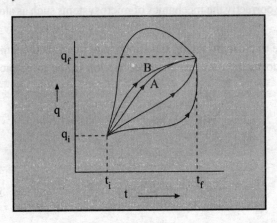

Fig. 8

The Hamilton's Principle of Least Action states that the realised path (or trajectory) actually followed by the system will be that along which the action integral is an extremum (that is it is stationary). Introducing the notation δ meaning variation, the principle states that

$$\delta \int_{t_i}^{t_f} L[q(t), \dot{q}(t), t]dt = 0$$

with

$$\delta q(t_i) = 0 = \delta q(t_f)$$

which simply states mathematically that the action integral be required to be stationary under variations in the path which are arbitrary except for the end points which are kept fixed (not varied).

We are quite familiar with extremising functions $f(x)$ of a variable x from calculus. Extremising (finding maxima, minima or points of inflection) involve finding the stationary points of the function viz. values of x about which the variation in the function due to infinitesimal changes in x vanish

$$\delta f(x) = \frac{df}{dx} \delta x = 0$$

which involves finding the x values where $\frac{df}{dx} = 0$. But now we have the action integral S which is an integral of functions $q(t)$ [and $\dot{q}(t)$] that define a possible path. We have a function of a function which is called a functional and we have to find the function [the path] along which the functional is stationary. Problems of this kind belong to a chapter of mathematics called the calculus of variations which was developed by Leonard Euler, Lagrange and other mathematicians. After demonstrating how the Hamilton's Principle of Least Action via the Calculus of Variations gives us the Lagrange's Equations of Motion, we shall give a mundane illustration of the calculus of variations from Plane Geometry.

Thus we seek an expression for the variation δS of the Action Integral S [the functional of the function $q(t)$ defining the path] due to variation $\delta q(t)$ in the path. Thus, for instance, the two paths labelled A and B in the figure above are supposed to represent two neighbouring paths. Of course the infinitesimal difference $q_B(t) - q_A(t) = \delta q(t)$ had to be magnified so that you can clearly see the two paths. Note that we have ensured that $\delta q(t_i) = 0 = \delta q(t_f)$. We seek to impose the condition $\delta S = 0$ (stationarity) with respect to such variations in path for otherwise arbitrary paths. Accordingly we have the condition for stationarity

$$0 = \delta S = \delta \int_{t_i}^{t_f} dt L[q(t), \dot{q}(t)] = \int_{t_i}^{t_f} dt \left[\frac{\partial L}{\partial q} \delta q + \frac{\partial L}{\partial \dot{q}} \delta \dot{q} \right]$$

For any given variation δq in the path we know $\delta q(t)$ as a function of t as it is simply the difference of the two functions representing the neighbouring paths. Hence $\delta \dot{q}(t)$ is nothing but $\dfrac{d}{dt} \delta q(t)$.

Inserting this in the second term in the integrand in the last step of the previous equation, we arrive at

$$\int_{t_i}^{t_f} dt \frac{\partial L}{\partial \dot{q}} \delta \dot{q} = \int_{t_i}^{t_f} dt \frac{\partial L}{\partial \dot{q}} \frac{d}{dt} \delta q = \left. \frac{\partial L}{\partial \dot{q}} \delta q \right|_{t_i}^{t_f} - \int_{t_i}^{t_f} \frac{d}{dt} \left(\frac{\partial L}{\partial \dot{q}} \right) \delta q$$

$$= -\int_{t_i}^{t_f} \frac{d}{dt} \left(\frac{\partial L}{\partial \dot{q}} \right) \delta q(t)$$

where we have integrated by parts and have simply noticed that the integrated term is zero as the endpoints are fixed and the variation $\delta q(t_i) = 0 = \delta q(t_f)$. Implementing this in the condition for stationarity we obtain

$$0 = \delta S = \int_{t_i}^{t_f} dt \left[\frac{\partial L}{\partial q} - \frac{d}{dt} \frac{\partial L}{\partial \dot{q}} \right] \delta q(t)$$

Since the integral on the right hand side has to be zero for arbitrary variations $\delta q(t)$ the only way this can be possible is for the terms in the square brackets to vanish or

$$\frac{\partial L}{\partial q} = \frac{d}{dt} \frac{\partial L}{\partial \dot{q}}$$

This result known as the Euler-Lagrange equation in the Calculus of Variations is easily generalised to a system with f degrees of freedom since each independent generalised coordinate can be varied independently and hence we arrive at the Lagrange's Equations of Motion

$$\frac{\partial L}{\partial q_k} = \frac{d}{dt} \frac{\partial L}{\partial \dot{q}_k}$$

Thus we see that the Hamilton's Principle of Least Action is equivalent to Lagrange's Equations of Motion which in turn followed from Newton's Equation of Motion. The observant student will be able to connect the δq_k's considered here with the virtual displacements of the d'Alembert approach.

A simple illustration of the calculus of variations

What is the curve $y = y(x)$ in a plane along which the distance between two fixed points is the shortest?

The element of distance along a curve $y = y(x)$ in a two dimensional plane in the cartesian coordinate system is given via Pythagoras theorem by

$$ds = \sqrt{(dx)^2 + (dy)^2} = \sqrt{\left\{1 + \left(\frac{dy}{dx}\right)^2\right\}}\, dx$$

and thus the distance between two fixed points 1 and 2 is given by

$$\int_1^2 \sqrt{\left\{1 + \left(\frac{dy}{dx}\right)^2\right\}}\, dx$$

which we seek to minimise to find the corresponding $y(x)$. If we had to minimise $\int_1^2 f\left(y, \frac{\partial y}{\partial x}\right) dx$ we

would have arrived at the Euler-Lagrange equation $\dfrac{\partial f}{\partial y} = \dfrac{d}{dx}\dfrac{\partial f}{\partial\left(\dfrac{\partial y}{\partial x}\right)}$. Here f is analogous to L, y to q

and x to t of our earlier discussion. With $f = \sqrt{1 + \left(\dfrac{dy}{dx}\right)^2}$ we note that $\dfrac{df}{dy} = 0$ since f does not depend

on y at all but only on $\dfrac{dy}{dx}$. Also $\dfrac{\partial f}{\partial\left(\dfrac{\partial y}{\partial x}\right)} = \dfrac{\dfrac{dy}{dx}}{\sqrt{1 + \left(\dfrac{dy}{dx}\right)^2}}$ and thus the Euler-Lagrange equation is

$$\frac{d}{dx}\left[\frac{\dfrac{dy}{dx}}{\sqrt{1 + \left(\dfrac{dy}{dx}\right)^2}}\right] = 0 \;\Rightarrow\; \frac{d^2 y}{dx^2} = 0$$

The equation $\dfrac{d^2 y}{dx^2} = 0$ is readily solved to give $y = mx + c$ where m and c are constants of integration. We thus obtain the result that the shortest distance between two fixed points on a plane surface is a straight line.

□□□

Module Two

VIBRATIONS and WAVES

3

Vibrations

Section 1. SIMPLE HARMONIC MOTION

A particle of mass m moving in one dimension under the influence of a force proportional to the displacement x from a fixed point taken to be the origin ($x = 0$) and directed towards that point executes Simple Harmonic Motion.

This may, for example, be taken to be the idealized limit of a block of mass m on a smooth frictionless horizontal plane attached by a spring to a point fixed on the vertical wall as shown in Fig. 1. Since the force of gravity on the block is balanced by the reaction of the plane on the block the only force acting on the block is that due to the spring which (if the spring is ideal) will be proportional to the extension x (x positive) trying to restore the spring to its relaxed length L_0. The constant of proportionality k (known as the Hooke's constant) is the stiffness of the spring and hence $F = -kx$ is the force along the relevant horizontal x-axis the origin ($x = 0$) being taken at the point distant L_0 from the wall. The force is always one of restoration for if the spring is compressed (x is negative) the force will be away from the wall. We work in the ideal limit of the block being described as a particle, the spring providing the force being ideal and massless and there is no friction offered by the table to the motion of the particle.

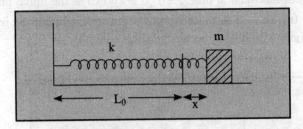

Fig. 1 A block moving under the action of a spring

The Newton's Equation governing this motion is thus

$$m\ddot{x} = -kx \qquad \qquad ...(1)$$

where $\dot{x} = \dfrac{dx}{dt}$ and $\ddot{x} = \dfrac{d^2x}{dt^2}$. Here x is the displacement of the particle, $\dot{x}$ the instantaneous velocity and $\ddot{x}$ the acceleration. It is convenient to divide the equation by m and to define $k/m = \omega^2$ and obtain

$$\ddot{x} = -\omega^2 x. \qquad \qquad ...(2)$$

Now since $\dfrac{d}{dt}\sin \omega t = \omega \cos \omega t$ and $\dfrac{d}{dt}\cos \omega t = -\omega \sin \omega t$ it is clear that $\sin \omega t$ and $\cos \omega t$ are both solutions of this differential equation which being of second order has two independent solutions. Since the equation is linear in x any linear combination of these two solutions is also a solution and hence the most general solution of the equation of motion is

$$x = A_1 \cos \omega t + A_2 \sin \omega t \qquad \qquad ...(3)$$

where A_1 and A_2 are constants whose values will dependent on the initial conditions, that is, say x and $\dot{x}$ at time $t = 0$.

It is more convenient to replace the constants A_1 & A_2 by the constants A and θ by defining

$$A_1 = A\sin\theta \text{ and } A_2 = A\cos\theta \qquad \qquad ...(4)$$

and thus

$$A_1^2 + A_2^2 = A^2\left(\sin^2\theta + \cos^2\theta\right) = A^2 \qquad \qquad ...(5)$$

and hence

$$A = \sqrt{A_1^2 + A_2^2} \text{ while the phase } \theta = \tan^{-1}\left(A_1/A_2\right) \qquad ...(6)$$

Accordingly the displacement is given as a function of time as

$$x = A\sin\theta\cos\omega t + A\cos\theta\sin\omega t = A\sin\left(\omega t + \theta\right) \qquad \qquad ...(7)$$

The $\begin{pmatrix}\text{maximum}\\\text{minimum}\end{pmatrix}$ value of x is $\begin{pmatrix}A\\-A\end{pmatrix}$ and the maximum displacement A is known as the **amplitude** and the system thus oscillates between $+A$ and $-A$. The angle θ measured in radians tells us through $x_0 = x(t=0) = A\sin\theta$ the displacement at time $t = 0$. θ is known as the initial phase. Thus with $\theta = 0$ we are reckoning time $t = 0$ with zero displacement to begin with, while if the initial phase were $\pi/2$ then at $t = 0$ the displacement would have been a maximum namely A.

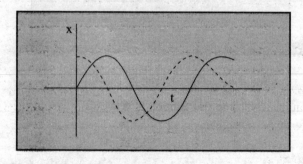

Fig. 2 Displacement (x) versus time (t) for a simple harmonic oscillator

The solid line corresponds to the initial phase $\theta = 0$ while the dotted line has initial phase $\theta = \pi/2$

The velocity of a particle undergoing simple harmonic motion is

$$\dot{x} = \frac{dx}{dt} = \omega A \cos\left(\omega t + \theta\right) \qquad \ldots(8)$$

the maximum value of which is ωA. Also noting that $\cos\left(\omega t + \theta\right) = \sin\left(\omega t + \theta + \pi/2\right)$ we see that the velocity leads the displacement by a phase of $\pi/2$. It is very important to remark that after a time $T = 2\pi/\omega$ the displacement and the velocity return to their previous values. This is simply because

$$\phi = \omega t + \theta \rightarrow \phi = \omega\left(t + \frac{2\pi}{\omega}\right) + \theta = \omega t + \theta + 2\pi$$ and the sine or cosine of any angle equal that of that

angle plus any integral multiple of 2π. Thus $x(t) = x(t + T)$. The time $T \equiv \dfrac{2\pi}{\omega}$ is known as the **periodic time** of the simple harmonic motion, and the full execution of this to and fro motion over that time T is known as a **cycle**.

A convenient geometric representation of simple harmonic motion is through what is known as the phase portrait or reference circle obtained by plotting $x = A \sin\left(\omega t + \theta\right)$ against $\dot{x}/\omega = A \cos\left(\omega t + \theta\right)$ which will be circle as $x^2 + \left(\dot{x}/\omega\right)^2 = A^2$ [the equation of the circle].

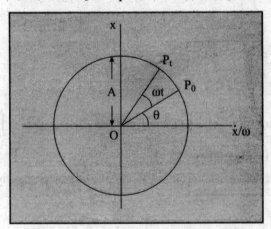

Fig. 3 The phase portrait or reference circle

Consider a representative point starting out at point P_0 at time $t = 0$ on this circle of radius A and imagine it to be turning with uniform angular velocity ω anti-clockwise along the circle. After a time t the radius vector will have moved to P_t where the angle $\lfloor P_t O P_0$ is ωt. The angle made with respect to the horizontal axis is now $\omega t + \theta$ and hence the projection of the radius vector OP_t on the vertical axis is $A \sin\left(\omega t + \theta\right)$ which is exactly what we obtained x to be for the simple harmonic oscillator. After a time $T = \dfrac{2\pi}{\omega}$ the representative point shall again return to P_0 and a cycle will have been completed.

It is useful to consider the energetics of simple harmonic motion. The concept of total energy and its conservation can be made to follow from Newton's equation of motion for any force which depends only on x (not on $\dot{x}$ or explicitly on time).

$$m\frac{d^2x}{dt^2} = F$$

multiply by $\frac{dx}{dt}$

$$m\frac{dx}{dt}\frac{d^2x}{dt^2} = F\frac{dx}{dt} \qquad \text{...(9)}$$

Integrate with respect to t from time t_1 to t_2, noting that $\frac{d}{dt}\left(\frac{dx}{dt}\right)^2 = 2\frac{dx}{dt}\frac{d}{dt}\left(\frac{dx}{dt}\right) = 2\frac{dx}{dt}\frac{d^2x}{dt^2}$

and that $\int F\frac{dx}{dt}dt = \int Fdx$ for the kind of force we are considering,

$$\frac{1}{2}m\left[\left(\frac{dx}{dt}\right)^2\right]_{t_1}^{t_2} - \int_{x_1}^{x_2} Fdx = 0 \qquad \text{...(10)}$$

The first term $\frac{1}{2}m\left[\left(\frac{dx}{dt}\right)^2\right]_{t_1}^{t_2} = \frac{1}{2}mv_2^2 - \frac{1}{2}mv_1^2$ is the change in kinetic energy $\frac{1}{2}mv^2$ (the energy

possessed by the particle by virtue of its motion) and the second term $-\int_{x_1}^{x_2} Fdx = V(x_2) - V(x_1)$ is the

change in potential energy (energy possessed by the particle by virtue of its position) or the work done

against the force over the displacement from x_1 to x_2. We thus note that the total energy

$$E = \frac{1}{2}m\left(\frac{dx}{dt}\right)^2 + V(x) \qquad \text{...(11)}$$

is independent of time. Since for the case at hand $F = -kx$, we have $V = -\int Fdx = \frac{1}{2}kx^2$ and therefore

$$E = \frac{1}{2}m\dot{x}^2 + \frac{1}{2}kx^2 = \frac{1}{2}m\left(\dot{x}^2 + \omega^2x^2\right) \qquad \text{...(12)}$$

(with $\omega = \sqrt{k/m}$) is a constant of the motion—the total energy.

For the oscillator with $x = A\sin(\omega t + \theta)$ the kinetic energy

$$k.e. = \frac{1}{2}m\dot{x}^2 = \frac{1}{2}mA^2\omega^2\cos^2(\omega t + \theta) \qquad \text{...(13)}$$

and the potential energy is

$$p.e. = \frac{1}{2}kx^2 = \frac{1}{2}m\omega^2 x^2 = \frac{1}{2}mA^2\omega^2 \sin^2(\omega t + \theta) \qquad ...(14)$$

So that the total energy E is a constant with respect to time

$$E = \frac{1}{2}mA^2\omega^2 \qquad ...(15)$$

The fact that the velocity is zero at maximum displacement for simple harmonic motion and is maximum when the displacement is zero shows how energy is being exchanged between potential and kinetic energy. The spring stores energy when it is compressed or extended and at the extremities of motion all the energy is potential and when it crosses $x = 0$ all the energy is kinetic.

Section 2. DAMPED SIMPLE HARMONIC MOTION

Simple harmonic motion was an idealization in that such a system would be executing oscillatory motion with constant amplitude A and constant total energy $E = \frac{1}{2}m\omega^2 A^2$ for all time to come. This is, of course, unrealistic as such motion is practically speaking, always damped. That is to say there must be another force which offers resistance to motion. Such forces are caused by friction or viscosity and for simplicity we shall take this force to be $-r\dot{x}$ viz. linearly dependent on the velocity, the constant of proportionality having the dimension of force per unit velocity. The minus sign signifies that this force is directed opposite to the velocity. According the equation of motion of such a damped simple harmonic oscillator is

$$m\ddot{x} = -kx - r\dot{x} \qquad ...(16)$$

Dividing by m and putting $\dfrac{k}{m} = \omega^2 (\mathrm{Dim}[\omega] = T^{-1})$ and $\dfrac{r}{m} \equiv \gamma (\mathrm{Dim}\,[\gamma] = T^{-1})$ we have to solve

$$\ddot{x} + \omega^2 x + \gamma\dot{x} = 0 \qquad ...(17)$$

The most efficient way to solve such equation is to make use of the exponential function and complex numbers [see Appendix I]. Let us attempt a trial solution of the form $x = Ce^{\alpha t}$ where C and α are constants. Since $\dfrac{dx}{dt} = \alpha Ce^{\alpha t}$ and $\dfrac{d^2 x}{dt^2} = \alpha^2 Ce^{\alpha t}$ we shall have a solution provided

$$Ce^{\alpha t}(\alpha^2 + \gamma\alpha + \omega^2) = 0$$

which is obtained by inserting the trial solution in equation (17). Of course $Ce^{\alpha t} \neq 0$ (which would otherwise gives a trivial result $x = 0$).

Thus we must have

$$\alpha^2 + \gamma\alpha + \omega^2 = 0 \qquad ...(18)$$

which being a quadratic equation for α gives two roots

$$\alpha = \frac{-\gamma \pm \sqrt{\gamma^2 - 4\omega^2}}{2} = \frac{-\gamma}{2} \pm \sqrt{\frac{\gamma^2}{4} - \omega^2} \qquad \ldots(19)$$

provided $\gamma^2 \neq 4\omega^2$, and hence we would obtain two independent solutions (as a second order differential equation should have). However in the case $\gamma^2 = 4\omega^2$ (which is called critical damping to be discussed later we must be careful. Depending on the parameters m, k, r (actually γ and ω) different solutions emerge:

Case I: Heavy (or Over) Damped Case $\gamma^2 > 4\omega^2$

Here we have two distinct real roots

$$\alpha_{\pm} = \frac{-\gamma}{2} \pm \sqrt{\frac{\gamma^2}{4} - \omega^2}$$

and hence the most general solution is

$$x = C_+ e^{\alpha_+ t} + C_- e^{\alpha_- t} = e^{-\frac{\gamma t}{2}} \left(C_+ e^{+\left(\sqrt{\frac{\gamma^2}{4} - \omega^2}\right) t} + C_- e^{-\left(\sqrt{\frac{\gamma^2}{4} - \omega^2}\right) t} \right) \qquad \ldots(20)$$

Note that this represents non-oscillatory solutions and the constants $\dot{C}_+$ and C_- will be fixed by the way we start off the system (initial conditions). Observe that since $\sqrt{\frac{\gamma^2}{4} - \omega^2} < \frac{\gamma}{2}$ as $t \rightarrow \infty$ whatever be C_+ and C_- $x \rightarrow 0$ so we do have damped solutions and the particle ultimately comes to rest at $x = 0$. Suppose the particle is resting at $x = 0$ and at time $t = 0$ is given a kick so that it starts off with $\dot{x} = u$ (say). It is often profitable to work with combinations of exponential functions e^{ξ} and $e^{-\xi}$ by introducing $\cosh \xi = \frac{1}{2}\left(e^{\xi} + e^{-\xi}\right)$ and $\sinh \xi = \frac{1}{2}\left(e^{\xi} - e^{-\xi}\right)$ which are called hyperbolic functions [see Appendix I].

This is because $\cosh \xi = 1$ and $\sinh \xi = 0$ at $\xi = 0$, and $\frac{d}{d\xi} \cosh \xi = \sinh \xi$ and $\frac{d}{d\xi} \sinh \xi = \cosh$ ξ. Also $e^{\pm \xi} = (\cosh \xi \pm \sinh \xi)$. Accordingly reorganising the terms in equation (20) we have

$$x = e^{-\frac{\gamma}{2}t}\left[C_1 \cosh\left\{\left(\sqrt{\frac{\gamma^2}{4} - \omega^2}\right)t\right\} + C_2 \sinh\left\{\left(\sqrt{\frac{\gamma^2}{4} - \omega^2}\right)t\right\}\right] \qquad \ldots(21)$$

where we have put $C_+ = \frac{C_1 + C_2}{2}$ and $C_- = \frac{C_1 - C_2}{2}$ for convenience.

Imposing now the initial condition of $x = 0$ and $\dot{x} = u$ at time $t = 0$ clearly we must put $C_1 = 0$ and our physically applicable solution in this case is

$$x = C_2 e^{-\gamma t} \sinh \left\{ \left(\sqrt{\frac{\gamma^2}{4} - \omega^2} \right) t \right\} \qquad ...(22)$$

with C_2 to be fixed using the condition $\dot{x}(t = 0) = u$.

The dependence on time of the displacement of an originally resting initially kicked over-damped simple harmonic oscillator is shown in Fig. 4.

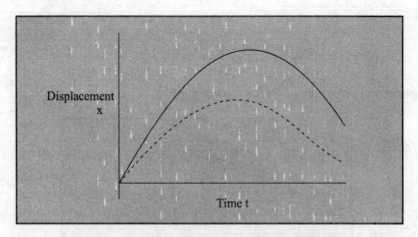

Fig. 4 Over-damped simple harmonic oscillator

The solid line corresponds to a larger damping constant γ than that depicted by the dotted line. The slope of the tangents to the curves at the origin are given by u, the initial velocity. The maximum displacement achieved can easily be calculated by located the maxima of the curves.

Case II: Critical damping $\gamma^2 = 4\omega^2$

In this case since the discriminant $\gamma^2 - 4\omega^2$ of the quadratic equation [equation (18)] vanishes the two roots $\alpha_\pm$ merge to a single one, namely, $\alpha_+ = \alpha_- = \dfrac{-\gamma}{2}$.

Thus we are apparently left with only one solution $x = Ce^{\frac{-\gamma}{2}t}$. However a second order equation must have two independent solutions and hence this is an unsatisfactory state of affairs until we recognise that the second derivative with respect to time of t is zero and hence C which we have so far taken to be a constant could very well be $A + Bt$ with A and B time independent. We can easily verify that at critical damping $\left(\gamma^2 = 4\omega^2 \right)$

$$x = (A + Bt)e^{\frac{-\gamma}{2}t} \qquad ...(23)$$

is indeed a solution of equation (18), namely, $\ddot{x} + \dfrac{\gamma^2}{4} x + \gamma \dot{x} = 0$.

Critical damping is of practical importance in the design of instruments such as the ballistic galvanometer which should respond to an initial push and return to zero displacement after showing its maximum displacement in the minimum possible time. Zero displacement at $t = 0$ implies that $A = 0$.

Hence the relevant solution is

$$x = Bte^{\frac{-\gamma}{2}t} \qquad \qquad ...(24)$$

for which the maximum occurs when

$$\frac{dx}{dt} = Be^{\frac{-\gamma}{2}t} - Bt\frac{\gamma}{2}e^{\frac{-\gamma}{2}t} = 0 \text{ or at } t = \frac{2}{\gamma}$$

The displacement versus time curve is shown in Fig. 5.

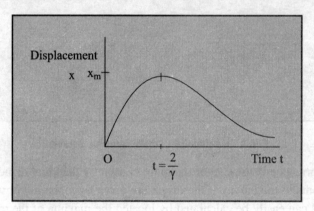

Fig. 5 Critically damped oscillator with $x(t = 0) = 0$

Case III: Under damped simple harmonic motion $\gamma^2 < \omega^2/4$

In this important case which leads to oscillatory but damped motion the discriminant of the quadratic equation [equation (18)] is negative and hence the roots $\alpha_{\pm}$ are complex namely

$$\alpha_{\pm} = \frac{-\gamma}{2} \pm i\sqrt{\omega^2 - \frac{\gamma^2}{4}} \qquad \qquad ...(25)$$

where $i = \sqrt{-1}$ (see Appendix I)

Thus the most general solution under these circumstances will be

$$x = C_+ e^{\alpha_+ t} + C_- e^{\alpha_- t} = e^{\frac{-\gamma}{2}t}\left(C_+ e^{i\left(\sqrt{\omega^2 - \frac{\gamma^2}{4}}\right)t} + C_- e^{-i\left(\sqrt{\omega^2 - \frac{\gamma^2}{4}}\right)t} \right)$$

However x being a displacement has to be real which implies that $C_- = C_+^*$ (where C_+^* is the complex conjugate of C_+ viz. $i \to -i$). In order to make the solution for the damped case tend to that which we had obtained in the undamped case we may take $C_+ = \dfrac{A}{2i} e^{i\theta}$ and hence $C_- = C_+^* = \dfrac{-A}{2i} e^{-i\theta}$ and this yields

$$x = A e^{\frac{-\gamma}{2}t} \frac{1}{2i} \left(e^{i(\tilde{\omega}t + \theta)} - e^{-i(\tilde{\omega}t + \theta)} \right)$$

$$= A e^{\frac{-\gamma}{2}t} \sin(\tilde{\omega}t + \theta) \qquad \qquad \dots(26)$$

where $\tilde{\omega} = \sqrt{\omega^2 - \gamma^2/4}$. Thus we see that the effect of damping (in the under-damped case) is two fold :

(a) The amplitude effectively decreases exponentially with time.

(b) The angular frequency undergoes a downward shift due to the damping $\omega \to \tilde{\omega} = \sqrt{\omega^2 - \gamma^2/4}$ and consequently there is an increase in the periodic time.

For the sake of concreteness choosing the initial phase θ to be $\pi/2$ in the solution for the under-damped harmonic oscillator equation (26) gives us

$$x = A e^{\frac{-\gamma}{2}t} \cos(\tilde{\omega}t) = A e^{-t/2\tau_d} \cos\left(2\pi \frac{t}{\tilde{T}} \right) \qquad \dots(27)$$

Putting $\tau_d \equiv \dfrac{1}{\gamma}$ and $\tilde{T} = \dfrac{2\pi}{\tilde{\omega}}$

We arrive at the pictorial representation of displacement versus time as shown in Fig. 6.

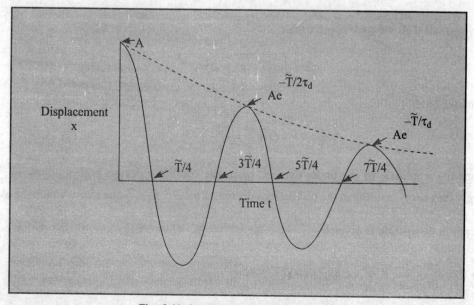

Fig. 6 Under-damped harmonic oscillator

The **logarithmic decrement** δ which is a measure of the rate at which the amplitude of a damped oscillator decays with time is the natural log of the ratio of the displacement at two successive peaks which are separated in time by one period $\tilde{T}$.

Thus

$$\delta = \ln\left(\frac{A_n}{A_{n+1}}\right) = \frac{1}{2}\frac{\tilde{T}}{\tau_d} = \frac{\tilde{T}\gamma}{2} = \frac{r\tilde{T}}{2m} \qquad \text{...(28)}$$

A related measure is what is known as the **relaxation time** which is the time taken for the decaying amplitude of oscillation $Ae^{-t/2\tau_d}$ to fall to $\frac{1}{e}$ of its initial value namely $2\tau_d = 2/\gamma = 2\frac{m}{r}$.

Next we introduce the concept of the **Quality factor** or **Q-value** of an under-damped simple harmonic oscillator which is but a measure of the ratio of the energy stored in the oscillator (manifested in its vibrations) to the energy lost per cycle (exhibited by the decay in its amplitude). From the solution for the under-damped simple harmonic oscillator $x = Ae^{\frac{-\gamma}{2}t}\sin(\tilde{\omega}t + \theta)$ we see that the amplitude of oscillation decays exponentially with time as $Ae^{\frac{-\gamma}{2}t}$ and hence the energy which is proportional to the square of the amplitude decays as

$$E = E_0 e^{-\gamma t} \quad \text{with} \quad \gamma = r/m \qquad \text{...(29a)}$$

The time for the energy to have decayed to $\frac{1}{e}$ of its initial value is $\tau_d = 1/\gamma = m/r$. In this time the angle in radians executed by the oscillator is

$$\tilde{\omega}\tau_d = \tilde{\omega}/\gamma = \frac{\tilde{\omega}m}{r} = Q. \qquad \text{...(29b)}$$

If r is small then we may approximate

$$\tilde{\omega} \equiv \sqrt{\omega^2 - 4\gamma^2} \simeq \omega = \sqrt{\frac{Q}{m}} \qquad \text{...(29c)}$$

Thus we have

$$Q \simeq \frac{\omega}{\gamma} = \frac{\omega m}{r} \qquad \text{...(29d)}$$

Since the amplitude of the under-damped harmonic oscillator decays with time as $Ae^{-\gamma t/2}$ and accordingly the energy residing in the oscillations decreases as $E = E_0 e^{-\gamma t}$ the rate at which the oscillator loses energy in dissipation is given by $\left|\frac{dE}{dt}\right| = \left|-\gamma E_0 e^{-\gamma t}\right| = \gamma E$. Thus energy loss by dissipation per cycle (in time $\tilde{T} = \frac{2\pi}{\tilde{\omega}} \simeq \frac{2\pi}{\omega}$ if $\gamma^2 \ll 4\omega^2$) is $\gamma E\tilde{T} = \gamma E \frac{2\pi}{\omega}$.

Thus

$$\frac{\text{Energy stored in oscillation by the system}}{\text{Energy loss per cycle}} = \frac{E}{\gamma E 2\,\pi/\omega} = \frac{\omega/\gamma}{2\pi} = Q \qquad \ldots(29e)$$

Section 3. FORCED DAMPED OSCILLATOR

We go on to consider the system of a particle (of mass m) oscillating under the influence of a restoring force ($-kx$ with k = stiffness constant) and a resistive or frictional dissipative force ($-r\dot{x}$) as before but further subjected to an alternating external force $F_0 \cos(\Omega t)$ where Ω is the angular frequency associated with the forcing term. Thus the equation of motion governing the system is

$$m\ddot{x} + r\dot{x} + kx = F_0 \cos(\Omega t) \qquad \ldots(30)$$

or, introducing the natural angular frequency $\omega = \sqrt{k/m}$ of the oscillator, the damping constant $\gamma \equiv r/m$ the equation becomes

$$\ddot{x} + \gamma\dot{x} + \omega^2 x = \frac{F_0}{m} \cos(\Omega t). \qquad \ldots(31)$$

One may note at the very outset that given a solution of equation (31) we may add to it any solution of its corresponding homogenous equation

$$\ddot{x} + \gamma\dot{x} + \omega^2 x = 0 \qquad \ldots(32)$$

and it still remains a solution. However as we have already seen these damp out with time and give rise to transients. We shall for the present concentrate on the long term steady solution of equation (31).

It is convenient to solve such equations using the method of complex variables by introducing $z = x + iy$ and noting that the above equation [equation (31)] is but the real part of the equation

$$\ddot{z} + \gamma\dot{z} + \omega^2 z = \frac{F_0}{m} e^{i\Omega t} \qquad \ldots(33)$$

Let us thus start with a steady state (non decaying) trial solution

$$z = A e^{i\Omega t} \qquad \ldots(34)$$

where A is a "complex amplitude". Of course this need not bother us as ultimately we shall look for $x = Re[z]$ viz. the real part of the complex variable z.

Since $\dot{z} = i\Omega A e^{i\Omega t}$ and $\ddot{z} = -\Omega^2 A e^{i\Omega t}$, substituting these in equation (33), yields

$$(-\Omega^2 + i\Omega\gamma + \omega^2) A e^{i\Omega t} = \frac{F_0}{m} e^{i\Omega t}$$

As the common factor $e^{i\Omega t}$ can be safely cancelled and as a result we have

$$A = \frac{F_0/m}{i\Omega\gamma + (\omega^2 - \Omega^2)} \qquad \text{...(35)}$$

$$= \frac{-iF_0}{\Omega\left[r - i\dfrac{k}{\Omega} + im\Omega\right]}$$

where in the last step we have multiplied numerator and denominator by $-i$, exported the factor of m to the denominator and used $\gamma m = r$ (the 'resistive' term), taken out a factor of Ω from the denominator and used $\omega^2 = k/m$. All this juggling has been done to use an analogy with electric circuits involving resistive, capacitive and inductive components with an alternating voltage supply which we shall discuss in detail in the next section.

Thus the steady state displacement x will be obtained by considering the real part of

$$z = Ae^{i\Omega t} = -\frac{iF_0 e^{i\Omega t}}{\Omega Z_m} \qquad \text{...(36a)}$$

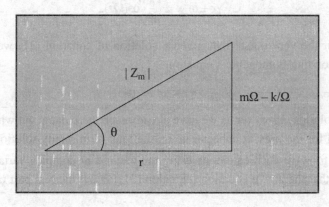

Fig. 7

where Z_m the complex 'impedance' is given by

$$Z_m = r - i\frac{k}{\Omega} + im\Omega = \sqrt{r^2 + \left(\Omega m - \frac{k}{\Omega}\right)^2}\, e^{i\theta} = |Z_m|e^{i\theta} \qquad \text{...(36b)}$$

where

$$\theta = \tan^{-1}\left(\frac{m\Omega - k/\Omega}{r}\right)$$

Putting it all together the solution of equation (33) for z

$$z = \frac{-iF_0 e^{i(\Omega t - \theta)}}{\Omega|Z_m|} \qquad \text{...(37)}$$

The reactive part of the impedance $(m\Omega - k/\Omega)$ leads to a phase difference of θ between the displacement and the force; the overall $- i$ causes a further lag of $\pi/2$ in the phase; and

$$x = \frac{F_0 \sin(\Omega t - \theta)}{\Omega |Z_m|} = \frac{F_0 \sin(\Omega t - \theta)}{\Omega \sqrt{r^2 + \left(\Omega m - \dfrac{k}{\Omega}\right)^2}} \qquad \text{...(38)}$$

The velocity of the particle undergoing forced vibration would than in the steady state be given by

$$\dot{x} = \frac{F_0 \cos(\Omega t - \theta)}{\sqrt{r^2 + \left(\Omega m - \dfrac{k}{\Omega}\right)^2}} \qquad \text{...(39)}$$

The study of equations (39) and (38) reveals all there is in the interesting phenomena of velocity and displacement resonances. First look at the amplitude of the velocity vide equation. (39) [viz. the coefficient of $\cos(\Omega t - \theta)$].

$$A_v = \frac{F_0}{\sqrt{r^2 + \left(\Omega m - \dfrac{k}{\Omega}\right)^2}} \qquad \text{...(40)}$$

One notices directly that this velocity amplitude becomes a maximum at $\Omega m = \dfrac{k}{\Omega}$ or $\Omega = \sqrt{\dfrac{k}{m}} = \omega$ as the impedance achieves it minimum value, namely, r. Thus the peak value of the velocity amplitude is F_0/r and occurs when the driving frequency Ω equals the natural frequency of the system. This is the so called velocity **resonance**. Also note as depicted in Fig. 8 that the velocity amplitude is symmetric about the peak position.

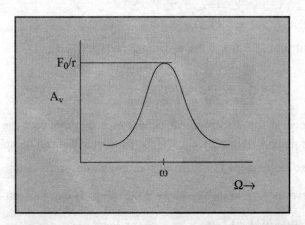

Fig. 8 Velocity amplitude versus forcing frequency showing
the resonance at the natural frequency ω of the system

Furthermore it may be observed that at resonance when $\Omega = \omega = \sqrt{k/m}$ the phase angle

$\theta = \tan^{-1}\left(\dfrac{m\Omega - k/\Omega}{r}\right)$ vanishes and the velocity and the forcing field goes quite in step with each other. With the forcing frequency above or below the resonant frequency there is a phase lag or a phase advance.

Turning our attention from the velocity of the forced damped oscillator to the displacement we examine equations (38) and (39). Here we note two features. The displacement has a $\sin(\Omega t - \theta)$ as contrasted with the $\cos(\Omega t - \theta)$ for the velocity [vide equation (39)]. This implies in fact that the phase of the displacement is exactly $\dfrac{\pi}{2}$ radians (or 90°) behind that of the velocity.

Furthermore the amplitude of the displacement [vide coefficient of $\sin(\Omega t - \theta)$ in equation (38)] is

$$A_x = \frac{F_0}{\Omega\sqrt{r^2 + \left(\Omega m - \dfrac{k}{\Omega}\right)^2}} \qquad \dots(41)$$

Here observe the extra factor of Ω in the denominator as compared to A_v given by equation (40). This has two important consequences. The position of the resonance is displaced and the peak (see Fig. 9) is no longer symmetric as shown in Fig. 8 but is skewed. Indeed the maximum of the amplitude pertaining to the displacement [A_x given by equation (41)] is given by the minimum of the denominator with respect to Ω (the driving frequency)

$$\frac{d}{d\Omega}\left[\Omega\sqrt{r^2 + \left(\Omega m - \frac{k}{\Omega}\right)^2}\right] = \frac{d}{d\Omega}\sqrt{\Omega^2 r^2 + \left(\Omega^2 m - k\right)^2} = 0$$

or $\qquad\qquad 2\Omega r^2 + 2(\Omega^2 m - k)2\Omega = 0$

which has the irrelevant root $\Omega = 0$ and the resonance occurs when

$$\Omega = \sqrt{\frac{k}{m} - \frac{r^2}{2m}} = \sqrt{\omega^2 - \frac{r^2}{2m}} \qquad \dots(42)$$

Thus the resonance in the displacement occurs at a frequency of the driving force which is slightly lower than the natural frequency $\omega = \sqrt{k/m}$ particularly if the damping is small or the mass parameter is large. Also because of the form of the amplitude A_x [equation 41] as compared to A_v [equation (40)] the curve for A_x versus Ω shows a skewness as can be seen from Fig. 9 note that as $\Omega \to 0$ A_x as per equation (41) $\to F_0/k$

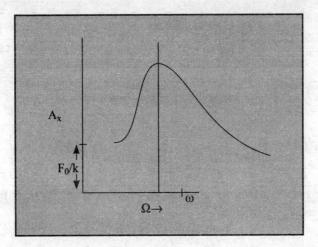

Fig. 9

The value of the peak displacement at resonance is given by putting $\Omega = \sqrt{\omega^2 - r^2/4m^2}$ in the expression for A_x given by equation (41) and one obtains

$$x_{\text{peak}} = \frac{F_0}{r\sqrt{\omega^2 - r^2/4m^2}} \qquad ...(43)$$

The peak displacement can be reduced by increasing the resistive factor r (damping) and this finds an application in the design of vibration free tables for sensitive equipment to provide insulation from vibration of the floor.

On the other hand a small value of r produces a high peak displacement and this is employed in making highly selective tuned radio circuits with large amplification at resonance.

We go on to show that after the transients have subsided and the steady state has been reached the driven oscillator adjusts itself in phase and amplitude such that the average power supplied by the driving force per cycle equals the energy dissipated through friction.

Since instantaneous power P (or rate of doing work) is the product of the instantaneous driving force $F_0 \cos \Omega t$ and the instantaneous velocity [given by equation (39)] at any given time t

$$P(t) = F_0 \cos \Omega t \frac{F_0}{|Z_m|} \cos (\Omega t - \theta) \qquad ...(44)$$

The average power $\bar{P}$ expended is thus the total work done in an oscillation divided by the period $T = \frac{2\pi}{\Omega}$. Thus

$$\bar{P} = \frac{1}{T} \int_0^T P(t)dt = \frac{F_0^2}{|Z_m| T} \int_0^T \cos \Omega t \cos(\Omega t - \theta)dt$$

$$= \frac{F_0^2}{|Z_m| T} \int_0^T \cos \Omega t [\cos \Omega t \cos \theta + \sin \Omega t \sin \theta] dt = \frac{F_0^2}{|Z_m|} \cos \theta \qquad ...(45)$$

as

$$\frac{1}{T} \int_0^T \cos^2 \Omega t \, dt = \frac{1}{T} \int_0^T \frac{1}{2}(\cos 2\Omega t + 1) dt = \frac{1}{2}$$

while

$$\int_0^T \cos \Omega t \sin \Omega t \, dt = \int_0^T \frac{1}{2} \sin 2\Omega t \, dt = 0$$

On the other hand since at any instant power or rate of doing work is force into velocity, the power expended in overcoming friction is

$$(r\dot{x})\dot{x} = r\dot{x}^2 = r \frac{F_0^2}{|Z_m|^2} \cos^2(\Omega t - \theta) \qquad ...(46)$$

Now

$$\frac{1}{T} \int_0^T dt \cos^2(\Omega t - \theta) = \frac{1}{T} \int_0^T dt \frac{1}{2}[1 + \cos\{2(\Omega t - \theta)\}]$$

$$= \frac{1}{2} + \frac{1}{4T}[\sin\{2(\Omega T - \theta)\} - \sin(2\theta)] = \frac{1}{2}$$

as

$$2\Omega T = 2\Omega \frac{2\pi}{\Omega} = 4\pi \quad \text{and} \quad \sin(4\pi - 2\theta) = \sin(-2\theta) = -\sin 2\theta$$

Thus the average over a period of the power expended in overcoming friction is $\dfrac{1}{2} \dfrac{rF_0^2}{|Z_m|^2}$. Now

refer to Fig. 8 and observe that $\dfrac{r}{Z_m} = \cos \theta$ and thus the power being expended in overcoming friction is

$$\frac{1}{2} \frac{F_0^2}{|Z_m|} \cos \theta \qquad ...(47)$$

which is exactly what we obtained for the average power supplied [see equation (45)].

It is worthwhile to study average power supplied $\bar{P}$ to the oscillator as a function of frequency of

the supply. Noting that $\bar{P} = \dfrac{F_0^2}{2|Z_m|} \cos \theta$ we see that this is a maximum when $\theta = 0$ which refering to

Fig. 8 corresponds to $m\Omega - k/\Omega = 0$ or $\Omega = \omega$ and there $|Z_m|$ has the minimum value of r, and the force and the velocity are in phase (marching in step with each other). Indeed

$$\bar{P}_{max} = \frac{F_0^2}{2r} \qquad ...(48)$$

at the frequency (Ω) of the supply equalling the natural frequency (ω) of the system where the velocity is a maximum. Thus the power absorption curve of the oscillator is shown below in Fig. (10).

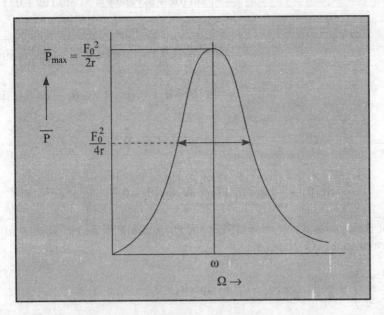

Fig. 10 Average power $\overline{P}$ as a function of the supply frequency Ω. The band width shown by $\leftrightarrow$ is the full width of the power absorption curve at half maximum

Section 4. SUPERPOSED SIMPLE HARMONIC MOTION IN TWO ORTHOGONAL DIRECTIONS (LISSAJOUS FIGURES)

Consider a particle subjected to a force along the X-axis leading to simple harmonic motion along that direction viz.

$$x = A_1 \sin (\omega_1 t + \theta_1) \qquad \qquad ...(49a)$$

and simultaneous along the Y-axis such that

$$y = A_2 \sin (\omega_2 t + \theta_2) \qquad \qquad ...(49b)$$

This for example can be conveniently arranged in a cathode ray oscilloscope by imposing an alternating voltage of frequency ω_1 across the horizontal plates and of frequency ω_2 across the vertical plates so that the electrons in the electron beam shall be moving in accordance to equations (49a) and (49b), and falling upon the screen.

If one eliminates the variable t (the time) using these two equations one obtains a relationship involving the variables x and y and the constants $A_1, A_2, \omega_1, \omega_2, \theta_1$ and θ_2. Indeed this equation would in general represent the resultant orbit in the XY-plane. For arbitrary ω_1 and ω_2 the curve could be very complicated. However, if ω_1 and ω_2 are commensurate, that is their ratio is rational viz. a ratio of two integers than and only then the curve in the XY-plane are closed and these are known as Lissajous figures.

Let us begin with the simplest case

$$\omega_1 = \omega_2 = \omega$$

$$x = A_1 \sin(\omega t + \theta_1) \text{ and } y = A_2 \sin(\omega t + \theta_2) \qquad \text{...(50a)}$$

Write

$$\frac{x}{A_1} = \sin(\omega t + \theta_1) = \sin \omega t \cos \theta_1 + \cos \omega t \sin \theta_1 \qquad \text{...(50b)}$$

$$\frac{y}{A_2} = \sin(\omega t + \theta_2) = \sin \omega t \cos \theta_2 + \cos \omega t \sin \theta_2 \qquad \text{...(50c)}$$

$$\frac{x}{A_1} \sin \theta_2 - \frac{y}{A_2} \sin \theta_1 = \sin \omega t \sin(\theta_2 - \theta_1) \qquad \text{...(51a)}$$

$$\frac{x}{A_1} \cos \theta_2 - \frac{y}{A_2} \cos \theta_1 = \cos \omega t \sin(\theta_1 - \theta_2) \qquad \text{...(51b)}$$

The sum of the squares of equations (51a) and (51b) result in the elimination of t and we get the equation of the orbit in the XY-plane.

$$\left(\frac{x}{A_1}\right)^2 + \left(\frac{y}{A_2}\right)^2 - \frac{2xy}{A_1 A_2} \cos(\theta_2 - \theta_1) = \sin^2(\theta_2 - \theta_1) \qquad \text{...(52)}$$

This is in general the equation of an ellipse with a tilted major axis. Putting $\theta_2 - \theta_1 = \dfrac{\pi}{2}$ this takes the form of the standard ellipse viz. $\left(\dfrac{x}{A_1}\right)^2 + \left(\dfrac{y}{A_2}\right)^2 = 1$. It moreover $A_1 = A_2$ we have the equation of a circle.

With $\theta_2 - \theta_1 = 2n\pi$ $(n = 0, 1, 2, ...)$ we have $\left(\dfrac{x}{A_1} - \dfrac{y}{A_2}\right)^2 = 0$ or $y = \dfrac{A_2}{A_1} x$ a straight line while with $\theta_2 - \theta_1 = (2n+1)\pi$ $(n = 0, 1, 2, ...)$ we have $\left(\dfrac{x}{A_1} + \dfrac{y}{A_2}\right)^2 = 0$ or $y = -\dfrac{A_2}{A_1} x$ a straight line with opposite slope.

Thus figures such as these shown in Fig. 11 result depending on relative phases in the case $A_1 = A_2 = A$

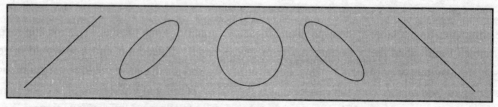

$\theta_2 - \theta_1 = 0 \qquad \theta_2 - \theta_1 = \dfrac{\pi}{4} \qquad \theta_2 - \theta_1 = \dfrac{\pi}{2} \qquad \theta_2 - \theta_1 = \dfrac{3\pi}{4} \qquad \theta_2 - \theta_1 = \pi$

Fig. 11 Lissajous figures with $\omega_1 = \omega_2$ and $A_1 = A_2$

To illustrate what happens (the sort of closed curves generated) when the two frequencies are commensurate (viz. are rational with respect to each other or ω_2/ω_1, is the ratio of two integers) let us take $\omega_1 = 2\omega_2 = 2\omega$ and for simplicity with take $\theta_1 = \theta_2$ and $A_1 = A_2 = A$. Thus with the two in phase

$$x = A\sin 2\omega t$$
$$y = A\sin \omega t$$

One can eliminate t between these two equations using trigonometric identities to arrive at the equation $4y^4 - 4A^2 y^2 + x^2 A^2 = 0$ and the corresponding Lissajous figure shown in Fig. 12.

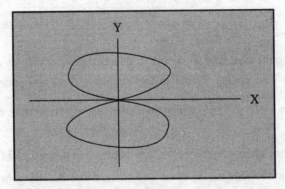

Fig. 12

Section 5. ANALOGY OF MECHANICAL AND ELECTRICAL OSCILLATIONS

We set out now to discuss the close analogy that exists between the voltage balance equation of the generic electric circuit shown below of a inductance (L), capacitor of capacity C, a resistance (R) connected to a oscillating voltage supply $V_0 \cos \Omega t$ and the forced damped oscillator governed by the force equation

$$m\ddot{x} + kx + R\dot{x} = F_0 \cos \Omega t \qquad \qquad ...(53)$$

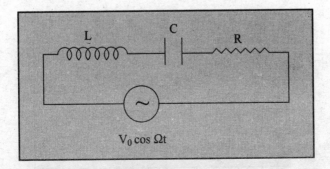

Fig. 13 The generic circuit of an alternating voltage source connected to L, C and R

The charge q is the analogue of the displacement x. Thus when a weightless spring of stiffness k is stretched by a displacement x the restoring force is $-kx$ and potential energy stored in it is $\frac{1}{2}kx^2$. When a capacitor of capacitance C is bestowed with a charge q the voltage across the plates is q/C and the electrical energy stored in the capacitor is $\frac{1}{2}\frac{q^2}{C}$. The analogy can even be brought closer by defining $C = 1/k$ for the spring viz. the reciprocal of the stiffness and by calling it the compliance. Similarly just as the capacitor stores electrical energy, the inductance stores magnetic energy. At any instant the induced voltage is

$$V = -L\frac{dI}{dt} = -L\frac{d^2q}{dt^2}$$

where I is the current and q the charge and $I = \dot{q}$ is the rate of flow of charge with time. The minus sign is because of Lenz's law. The energy stored in the magnetic field associated with the inductance is $\int |V| I \, dt = \int L\frac{dI}{dt} I \, dt = \frac{1}{2}LI^2 = \frac{1}{2}L\dot{q}^2$ which is analogous to the kinetic energy in the mechanical oscillator.

As far as the resistance is concerned the voltage across it is determined from Ohm's Law and thus $V = IR = R\dot{q}$ and this is analogous to the term due to resistive damping in the mechanical damped oscillator, namely, $r\dot{x}$.

Putting in all the terms we have the voltage balance equation

$$L\ddot{q} + \frac{q}{C} + R\dot{q} = V_0 \cos \Omega t \qquad \qquad ...(54)$$

which should be compared with the analogous mechanical system governed by equation (53).

It is worth looking at a few special cases. Thus for instance if $R = 0$ and if $V_0 = 0$ we have

$$L\ddot{q} + \frac{q}{C} = 0 \quad \text{or} \quad \ddot{q} = -\left(\frac{1}{\sqrt{LC}}\right)^2 q$$

which implies that a charged capacitor connected to an inductance would have its charge oscillating

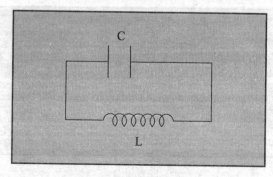

Fig. 14

with an angular frequency of $\omega = \dfrac{1}{\sqrt{LC}}$. The total energy would be a constant with the electrical energy stored in the capacitor (much like the potential energy in a stretched (or compressed) spring, going into the magnetic energy in the inductance (analogous to the kinetic energy of the particle executing simple harmonic motion) and back and forth with no damping whatsoever.

Again look at a circuit with a condenser with charge Q resident at time $t = 0$ being discharged

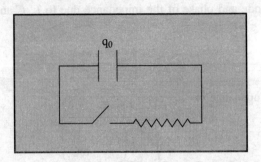

Fig. 15

being made to discharge through a resistor $\dfrac{q}{C} + R\dfrac{dq}{dt} = 0$. The second term representing the charge flowing through the resistor and losing the electrical energy stored in it through ohmic dissipation

$$\frac{dq}{dt} = -\frac{q}{RC}$$

which gives the solution $q = q_0\, e^{-t/RC}$ when we have inserted the initial condition $q = q_0$ at $t = 0$ to fix constant of integration. The time constant RC is characteristic of the RC circuit.

Indeed we can generalize Ohm's law $V = IR$ relating the voltage applied to the current flowing through it to the more general solution

$$V = IZ$$

where Z is called the impedance, even in the situation when the current I is alternating, say

$$I = I_0 e^{i\omega t}$$

Again we should remember that the physical current will be the real part of this expression.

Thus the voltage across inductance would be

$$V_L = L\frac{dI}{dt} = L\frac{d}{dt}I_0 e^{i\omega t} = (i\omega L)I_0 e^{i\omega t} = (i\omega L)I$$

which tells us that the magnitude of the voltage is ωL times that of the current and that the phase is 90° ahead of that of the current as $e^{i\pi/2} = i$.

Similarly the voltage across the condenser is

$$\frac{q}{C} = \frac{1}{C}\int I\, dt = \frac{1}{C}I_0\int e^{i\omega t} dt = \frac{1}{i\omega C}I_0 e^{i\omega t} = -\frac{iI}{\omega C}$$

as

$$\frac{1}{i} = -i = e^{-i\pi/2}$$

Hence the magnitude of the impedance due to a capacitor is $\frac{1}{\omega C}$ while the voltage lags in phase behind the current in the circuit by 90°.

Therefore the magnitude and phase of the impedance due to L, C and R in a circuit can be put together as an impedance

$$Z = R + i\left(\omega L - \frac{1}{\omega C}\right)$$

and the magnitude of the impedance is

$$|Z| = \sqrt{R^2 + \left(\omega L - \frac{1}{\omega C}\right)^2}$$

and its phase as

$$\tan^{-1}\left(\frac{\omega L - \frac{1}{\omega C}}{R}\right).$$

□□□

Appendix - I

SOME MATHEMATICAL TOOLS (USE OF COMPLEX VARIABLES)

Methods of complex variables are useful for solving equations that occur for simple harmonic oscillators, damped, forced etc., as also for the corresponding electrical analogues involving inductances L, capacitors C and resistances R and driving alternating voltages $V_0 \cos \Omega t$.

Every complex number z can be written in the Cartesian form $z = x + iy$ where x and y are both real and $i = \sqrt{-1}$. Thus $i^2 = -1$ and $\frac{1}{i} = -i$. The sum of two complex numbers is a complex number.

Thus with $z_1 = x_1 + iy_1$ and $z_2 = x_2 + iy_2$ we have $z_1 + z_2 = (x_1 + x_2) + i\,(y_1 + y_2)$. The product of two complex numbers $z_1 z_2$ is easily worked out to give $z_1 z_2 = (x_1 + iy_1)\,(x_2 + iy_2) = (x_1 x_2 - y_1 y_2) + i\,(x_1 y_2 + y_1 x_2)$. If $z = x + iy$ the complex conjugate is defined by simple changing $i \rightarrow -i$ and is indicated by inserting a * viz. $z* = x - iy$. The product $zz* = (x + iy)\,(x - iy) = x^2 + y^2$ is real and the quantity $\sqrt{zz*} = \sqrt{x^2 + y^2}$ is written as $|z|$ and is called the absolute value or modulus of z.

A complex number is very conveniently represented by a point (x, y) in a two dimensional plane with its abscissa (x) equal to the real part and its imaginary part (y) as its ordinate. The X-axis could also be called the real axis and the Y-axis the imaginary axis. The length of the line segment joining the origin of coordinates to the point $z(x, y)$ is given by the Pythagoras Theorem as $\sqrt{x^2 + y^2}$ which is $\sqrt{zz*} = |z|$ is the absolute value or modulus of z. Furthermore if this line joining the origin to the point z makes an angle θ with respect to the positive X direction then clearly $x = r \cos\theta$ and $y = r \sin\theta$ where $r = |z| = \sqrt{x^2 + y^2}$ is also called the radial coordinate of the point representing the complex number.

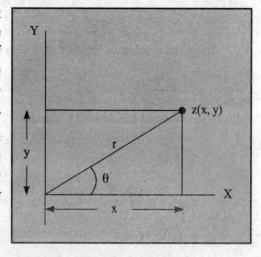

Fig. 16 The Argand diagram

The so-called polar angle is $\theta = \tan^{-1}(y/x)$. Indeed (r, θ) the polar coordinates may also be used in describing points in a plane in place of the Cartesian coordinates (x, y). In this context r is refered to as the magnitude and θ the phase of the complex number z.

Next we note the introduction of the exponential function e^{ξ} by Leonard Euler through the convergent series

$$e^{\xi} = 1 + \xi + \frac{\xi^2}{2!} + \frac{\xi^3}{3!} + \ldots$$

with the beautiful property that $\dfrac{d}{d\xi} e^{\xi} = e^{\xi}$ as can readily be checked. Furthermore this enabled us to relate exponential functions to trigonometric functions as

$$e^{i\theta} = 1 + (i\theta) + \frac{(i\theta)^2}{2!} + \frac{(i\theta)^3}{3!} + \ldots$$

$$= \left(1 - \frac{\theta^2}{2!} + \ldots\right) + i\left(\theta - \frac{\theta^3}{3!} + \ldots\right)$$

where the real and imaginary terms in the series are written on two separate lines with a purpose.

The Taylor expansion of trigonometric functions are

$$\cos\theta = 1 - \frac{\theta^2}{2!} + \ldots$$

$$\sin\theta = \theta - \frac{\theta^3}{3!} + \ldots$$

and thus

$$e^{i\theta} = \cos\theta + i\sin\theta.$$

Therefore a complex number may also be expressed as

$$z = x + iy = r\cos\theta + ir\sin\theta = re^{i\theta} = |z|\,e^{i\theta}$$

which is known as the polar form of a complex number and the pictorial representation shown in Fig. 16 is known as the Argand Diagram.

4 *Waves*

Waves abound in nature. Surface waves in a fluid such as water, sound waves in a gas such as air, electromagnetic waves, de Broglie waves associated with particles in Quantum Mechanics etc. We show in the first two sections of this chapter, how such phenomena emerge from the classical mechanics of particles in the continuum limit. In section three we demonstrate how sound waves emerge in a gas. We go on to discuss thereafter generic features associated with waves.

Section 1. LONGITUDINAL WAVES

We start from a necklace of point particles (beads) each of mass m connected to each other by massless springs of length Δ which on elongation give rise to restoring forces proportional to the extension (with Hooke's constant k say). We then go on to a continuum limit by taking $m \to 0$ $\Delta \to 0$ such that $\dfrac{m}{\Delta} = \rho$ the mass per unit length of a string and thus arrive at a wave equation which illustrates longitudinal waves.

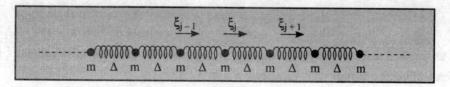

Fig. 1

Consider each bead displaced from its equilibrium (unstretched springs) by an amount ξ_j say in the case of the jth bead and so on for the others. Focussing on the representative j^{th} bead, it experiences a force $- k(\xi_j - \xi_{j+1})$ due to the extension of the spring connecting it to the neighbouring bead on its right and also a force $- k(\xi_j - \xi_{j-1})$ due to that joining it to the bead on the left. Consequently the Newton's equation of motion for the jth bead is

$$m\frac{d^2\xi_j}{dt^2} = k\{(\xi_{j+1} - \xi_j) - (\xi_j - \xi_{j-1})\} \qquad \qquad ...(1)$$

Now we wish to make this necklace of beads N in all, each of mass m, connected to each other by $(N-1)$ massless springs (each of unstretched length Δ) to approach a continuous string of length L. In order to do that we need to take $\Delta \to 0$ and $N \to \infty$ such that $(N-1)\,\Delta \to L$ and also take $m \to 0$ such that $m/\Delta \to \rho$ the mass per unit length of resulting string. Of course we could have $L \to \infty$ as well so that we have an infinitely long string and thus avoid worrying about end effects.

Of course here we must also ponder over the question : what happens to the stiffness constant k of the spring when we reduce its unstretched length. For a given force the extension of a spring is inversely proportional to its stiffness k. On the other hand the extension of the spring is directly proportional to its relaxed length. Therefore $k \propto \dfrac{1}{\Delta}$, for the springs we are considering. It is common experience that when you shorten a spring it gets stiffer. Thus in the limit $\Delta \to 0$ we must also take $k \to \infty$ such that $k\Delta \to \tau$ which is the tension of the resulting string. Since now we have a continuous string we must accordingly replace the discrete ordinal number of the bead (j) to the continuous variable x measured along the string.

Thus we have

$$\xi_j(t) \longrightarrow \xi(x,t) \qquad\qquad\qquad\qquad \text{...(2a)}$$

$$\xi_{j+1}(t) \to \xi(x+\Delta,t) = \xi(x,t) + \Delta\frac{\partial}{\partial x}\xi(x,t) + \frac{\Delta^2}{2}\frac{\partial^2}{\partial x^2}\xi(x,t) + ... \qquad\qquad \text{...(2b)}$$

$$\xi_{j+1}(t) \to \xi(x-\Delta,t) = \xi(x,t) - \Delta\frac{\partial}{\partial x}\xi(x,t) + \frac{\Delta^2}{2}\frac{\partial^2}{\partial x^2}\xi(x,t) + ... \qquad\qquad \text{...(2c)}$$

where we have merely instituted the appropriate Taylor's series.

These when inserted into Newton's equation for the discrete system [equation (1)] and the limit $\Delta \to 0$ (with $\dfrac{m}{\Delta} \to \rho$ and $k\Delta \to \tau$) results in the partial differential equation

$$\rho\frac{\partial^2}{\partial t^2}\xi(x,t) = \tau\frac{\partial^2}{\partial x^2}\xi(x,t) \qquad\qquad\qquad \text{...(3)}$$

This as we shall discuss is nothing but the wave equation for longitudinal waves (as ξ represents displacements **along** the string) with velocity $v = \sqrt{\tau/\rho}$ viz.

$$\left(\frac{\partial^2}{\partial x^2} - \frac{1}{v^2}\frac{\partial^2}{\partial t^2}\right)\xi(x,t) = 0. \qquad\qquad\qquad \text{...(4)}$$

Section 2. TRANSVERSE WAVES

To illustrate transverse waves we begin with transverse planar (with XY plane) oscillations along the Y-axis of point masses m tied at distance a from each other along the X-axis on a stretched massless string (with tension τ). We confine ourselves to small displacements along Y. Focussing our attention to the transverse motion (y_j) of the jth mass point we observe from Fig. 2, that the displacement along the transverse direction is controlled by the Y-component of the forces of tension from the string segments joining it to the particle on the left ($j-1$) and that to the right ($j+1$).

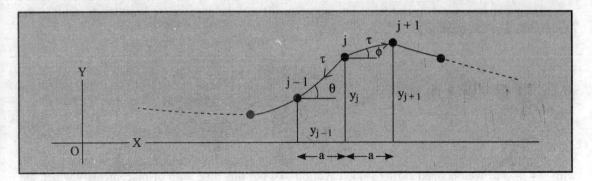

Fig. 2

The force controlling motion along the transverse direction (Y) of the jth bead is given by the component of the forces of tension on it along Y which is $\tau \sin \phi$ upwards and $- \tau \sin \theta$ (as it is downwards) and thus the Newton's equation for the jth mass point is

$$m\ddot{y}_j = \tau(\sin\phi - \sin\theta) \simeq \tau(\tan\phi - \tan\theta)$$

as for small amplitude displacements along Y the angles ϕ and θ are small and hence the angles in radians are approximately equal to the sine or tangents of the angles concerned).

Now $$\tan\phi = \frac{y_{j+1} - y_j}{a} \text{ and } \tan\theta = \frac{y_j - y_{j-1}}{a}$$

and hence we have

$$m\ddot{y}_j = \tau\left[\frac{y_{j+1} - y_j}{a} - \frac{y_j - y_{j-1}}{a}\right] = \tau\left[\frac{y_{j+1} + y_{j-1} - 2y_j}{a}\right]$$

we divide by a to get

$$\frac{m}{a}\ddot{y}_j = \tau\left(\frac{y_{j+1} + y_{j-1} - 2y_j}{a^2}\right) \qquad \ldots(5)$$

and promote j (the ordinal index of the mass point) to the continuous variable x as we take the continuum limit $a \to 0$, $m \to 0$, $\dfrac{m}{a} \to \rho$, we once again proceed as before using the Taylor expansion to assert that

$$y_i(t) \to y(x,t)$$

$$y_{i+1}(t) \to y(x+a,t) = y(x,t) + a\frac{\partial y}{\partial x}(x,t) + \frac{a^2}{2!}\frac{\partial^2 y}{\partial x^2}(x,t) + \ldots$$

$$y_{i-1}(f) \to y(x-a,t) = y(x,t) - a\frac{\partial y}{\partial x}(x,t) + \frac{a^2}{2!}\frac{\partial^2 y}{\partial x^2}(x,t) + \ldots$$

These expansions when instituted into equation (5) and the appropriate limit taken result in the partial differential equation

$$\rho \frac{\partial^2 y(x,t)}{\partial t^2} = \tau \frac{\partial^2 y}{\partial x^2}$$

which once again yields the equation

$$\left(\frac{\partial^2}{\partial x^2} - \frac{1}{v^2} \frac{\partial^2}{\partial t^2} \right) y(x,t) = 0 \qquad \qquad ...(6)$$

with $v = \sqrt{\dfrac{\tau}{\rho}}$ as we obtained earlier [vide equation (4)] but this time with displacements y which are transverse with respect to the x direction along which the wave travels. We thus have a transverse wave.

Section 3. COMPRESSIONAL WAVES IN GASES AND SOUND

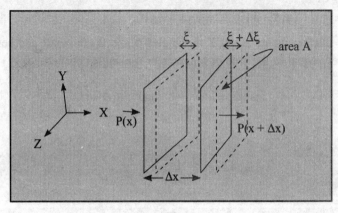

Fig. 3

Imagine a large plate vibrating in a region filled with gas at some equilibrium pressure P_0 and some density D_0. Consider the region between the planes of area A shown at x and $x + \Delta x$ parallel to vibrating plate with volume V_0. The vibration of the plate causes changes (dependent on x and time t) in pressure, volume and density of the gas

$$P_0 \rightarrow P = P_0 + p \qquad \qquad ...(7a)$$
$$V_0 \rightarrow V = V_0 + v \qquad \qquad ...(7b)$$
$$D_0 \rightarrow D = D_0 + \rho. \qquad \qquad ...(7c)$$

Normally in the case of compressional waves set up by vibrating plates or sound waves $p \ll P_0$, $v \ll V_0$, $\rho \ll D_0$.

The element of gas with cross-sectional area A and width Δx is our focus of attention. This has, to begin with, a volume $V_0 = A \Delta x$. Hence the mass of the gas between these two planes is $D_0 V_0$ and for a fixed mass of gas between the two planes being considered we must have

$$D_0 V_0 = DV = (D_0 + \rho)(V_0 + v) = D_0 V_0 \left(1 + \frac{\rho}{D_0} \right) \left(1 + \frac{v}{V_0} \right) \qquad \qquad ...(8)$$

Since $\dfrac{\rho}{D_0} \ll 1$ and $\dfrac{v}{V_0} \ll 1$, we have to a very good approximation

$$\frac{v}{V_0} = -\frac{\rho}{D_0} \qquad ...(9)$$

or in other words the fractional change in volume is approximately the negative of the fractional change in density. In the case of sound waves in air this is $\sim 10^{-3}$.

Responding to the vibration of the plate and impelled by the pressure gradient the molecules in the plane at X are displaced by $\xi(x, t)$ while those in the plane at $x + \Delta x$ suffer a displacement $\xi + \Delta \xi$

$= \xi + \dfrac{\partial \xi}{\partial x} \Delta x$ (working here and elsewhere to linear order in Δx). Thus there is an increase in the volume

of gas between the two planes by $A \dfrac{\partial \xi}{\partial x} \Delta x$.

Therefore the fractional change in volume of the gas in the region of concern, viz., the strain, is

$$\frac{v}{V_0} = \frac{A \dfrac{\partial \xi}{\partial x} \Delta x}{A \Delta x} = \frac{\partial \xi}{\partial x} = -\frac{\rho}{D_0} \qquad ...(10)$$

the last step follows by virtue of equation (9).

This strain is caused because the pressure along the X-axis is $P(x)$ for the plane on the left of the element of gas being considered and $P(x + \Delta x)$ on the plane on the right so that there is a net force acting on the gas element

$$A[P(x) - P(x + \Delta x)] = A \left[P(x) - \left\{ P(x) + \frac{\partial P}{\partial x} \Delta x \right\} \right]$$

$$= -A \frac{\partial P(x)}{\partial x} \Delta x = -A \frac{\partial p}{\partial x} \Delta x \qquad ...(11)$$

The last step follows as

$$P = P_0 + p$$

and P_0 is x independent.

The mass of the element is $AD_0 \Delta x$ (again to first order of smallness as ρ/D_0 is small) and the

acceleration of the element is approximately given by $\dfrac{\partial^2 \xi}{\partial t^2}$ and hence Newton's equation of motion

gives us

$$AD_0 \Delta x \frac{\partial^2 \xi}{\partial t^2} = -A \frac{\partial p}{\partial x} \Delta x$$

and thus we have

$$D_0 \frac{\partial^2 \xi}{\partial t^2} = -\frac{\partial p}{\partial x} \qquad ...(12)$$

To relate $\dfrac{\partial p}{\partial x}$ on the right hand side to the relative displacements of the layer of gas we note that the relevant elastic properties of the gas, viz. measure of its compressibility is encoded in its bulk modulus

$$B = \frac{\text{stress}}{\text{strain}} = -\frac{dP}{\left(\dfrac{dV}{V}\right)} = -V\frac{dP}{dV} \qquad \qquad ...(13)$$

namely the rate of the change in force per unit area divided by the change in volume per unit volume. For a perfect gas at a fixed temperature we have PV = constant (the Boyle's law) which gives the isothermal compressibility or Bulk Modulus to be P. However the time period associated with sound vibrations is too short for the exchange of heat (by diffusion, thermal conductivity and viscous forces) and so the conditions rather than being isothermal are actually adiabatic and we should rather use the

fact that PV^{γ} = constant where $\gamma = \dfrac{C_P}{C_V}$ the ratio of the specific heat at constant pressure to that at constant volume when $V^{\gamma}\,dP + \gamma PV^{\gamma-1}\,dV = 0$ and the adiabatic bulk modulus should be used

$$B_{ad} = -V\frac{dP}{dV} = \gamma P. \qquad \qquad ...(14)$$

Returning to the case at hand by virtue of equation (12) the stress which is the excess pressure dP or p is the negative of the Bulk Modulus times the strain which is $\dfrac{v}{V_0}$ and given by equation (10) to be $\dfrac{\partial \xi}{\partial x}$, viz.

$$p = -B_{ad}\frac{\partial \xi}{\partial x} \qquad \qquad ...(15)$$

which when substituted into the right hand side of the equation of motion [equation (12)] yields

$$D_0 \frac{\partial^2 \xi}{\partial t^2} = B_{ad}\frac{\partial^2 \xi}{\partial x^2}$$

Thus once again we arrive at a wave equation

$$\frac{\partial^2 \xi}{\partial x^2} - \frac{1}{C_s^2}\frac{\partial^2 \xi}{\partial t^2} = 0 \qquad \qquad ...(16)$$

where $\qquad\qquad C_s = \sqrt{\dfrac{B_{ad}}{D_0}} = \sqrt{\dfrac{\gamma P_0}{D_0}}$ [by equation (14)] is the velocity of sound in a gas.

Section 4. THE WAVE EQUATION

The generic form of the wave equation whether longitudinal, transverse or scalar (the last was the situation for the isotropic pressure wave in a gas) is

$$\frac{\partial^2 y}{\partial x^2} = \frac{1}{c^2}\frac{\partial^2 y}{\partial t^2} \qquad\qquad ...(17)$$

where $y = y(x,t)$ is a function of x and t.

We show that any function of the form $f(\eta)$ where $\eta = ct - x$ is a solution of the wave equation. This is easily seen by applying the chain rule of differentiation

$$\frac{\partial}{\partial t}y = \frac{\partial}{\partial t}f(\eta) = \left(\frac{d}{d\eta}f(\eta)\right)\frac{\partial\eta}{\partial t} = +c\frac{d}{d\eta}f(\eta)$$

$$\frac{\partial^2 y}{\partial t^2} = \frac{d}{d\eta}\left(+c\frac{d}{d\eta}f\right)\frac{\partial\eta}{\partial t} = c^2\frac{d^2}{d\eta^2}f(\eta)$$

$$\frac{\partial}{\partial x}y = \frac{\partial}{\partial x}f(\eta) = \left(\frac{d}{d\eta}f(\eta)\right)\frac{\partial\eta}{\partial x} = -\frac{d}{d\eta}f(\eta)$$

$$\frac{\partial^2}{\partial x^2}y = \frac{d}{d\eta}\left(-\frac{d}{d\eta}f\right)\frac{\partial\eta}{\partial x} = +\frac{d^2}{d\eta^2}f$$

$\therefore \quad f(\eta = ct - x)$ is a solution of the wave equation.

Proceeding in a similar manner it is easily established that any function of the form $f(\eta = ct + x)$ is also a solution of the wave equation.

As $f(ct - x)$ describes the form of the disturbance as a function of x and t, it may be noted that at a time $t + \Delta t$ the function has exactly the same, disposition at $x + c\Delta t$, that is the "wave" is moving rightwards

$$\because \qquad f[c(t + \Delta t) - (x + c\Delta t)] = f(ct - x)$$

with a velocity c; similarly the function $f(ct + x)$ describes a solution of the wave equation which is moving leftwards.

Since in our derivation of the wave equation along the string or in a gas the 'particles' at each location were executing simple harmonic motion it is suggestive to consider special solutions of the wave equation of the form $y = A\sin(\omega t - \theta) = A\sin\left[\dfrac{\omega}{c}(ct - x)\right]$ choosing the x dependence of θ to be

$\dfrac{\omega x}{c}$ in order to have a function of $ct - x$.

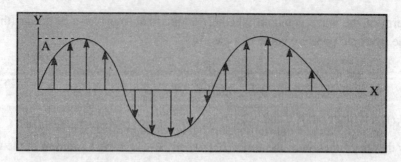

From the form of the function $\sin\left[\dfrac{\omega}{c}(ct - x)\right]$ we see that at each point x the oscillator executes simple harmonic motion of angular frequency ω, with period $\dfrac{2\pi}{\omega}$ and hence frequency $\nu = \dfrac{\omega}{2\pi}$. Moreover in x after a distance $\dfrac{\omega x}{c} = 2\pi$ the characteristics of displacement are repeated. This distance $x = \dfrac{2\pi c}{\omega} \equiv \lambda$ is known as the wavelength or with $\nu = \dfrac{\omega}{2\pi}$ we have with $\nu\lambda = c$. Also $\dfrac{2\pi}{\lambda} = k$ is known as the wave number of the wave. Note here and later the use of the Roman font k for the wave-number as distinguished from the italics k used earlier for the spring constant. Such waves are known as harmonic waves. Using these relations the wave may be written in several equivalent ways

$$y = A \sin\left[\dfrac{2\pi}{\lambda}(ct - x)\right] \qquad \qquad ...(18a)$$

$$y = A \sin\left[2\pi\left(\nu t - \dfrac{x}{\lambda}\right)\right] \qquad \qquad ...(18b)$$

$$y = A \sin(\omega t - kx) \qquad \qquad ...(18c)$$

The wave velocity (also known as the phase velocity) is the rate at which the disturbance (say the crest of the wave) moves and is clearly given by $\dfrac{dx}{dt}$ as for a fixed phase of the wave viz. equation (18a) which is clearly $ct - x =$ constant and hence $\dfrac{dx}{dt} = c$.

The waves represented by equations (18) are monochromatic waves, that is, waves of a fixed wavelength λ or frequency ν. Waves may be made to carry signals in the form of modulations in their amplitude. These are possible by superposing waves of different frequency (or wave groups). Thus for instance if we superpose two waves of the same amplitude but of angular frequency

$\omega_1 = \omega_0 + \dfrac{\Delta\omega}{2}$ and $\omega_2 = \omega_0 - \dfrac{\Delta\omega}{2}$ and correspondingly of wave number $k_1 = k_0 + \dfrac{\Delta k}{2}$ and $k_2 = k_0 - \dfrac{\Delta k}{2}$

then the resultant superposition would be

$$y = y_1 + y_2 = A\left\{ \sin\left[\left(\omega_0 + \dfrac{\Delta\omega}{2}\right)t - \left(k_0 + \dfrac{\Delta k}{2}\right)x\right] + \sin\left[\left(\omega_0 - \dfrac{\Delta\omega}{2}\right)t - \left(k_0 - \dfrac{\Delta k}{2}\right)x\right] \right\}$$

$$= 2A\cos(\Delta\omega t - \Delta k x)\sin(\omega_0 t - k_0 x) \qquad \ldots(19)$$

that is a slowly varying modulated amplitude (with $\Delta\omega$ and Δk small) forming the envelope of a rapidly

varying wave (with angular frequency and wave number ω_0 and k_0) as shown in Fig. 5.

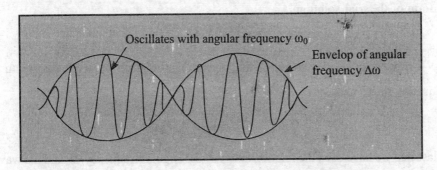

Oscillates with angular frequency ω_0

Envelop of angular frequency $\Delta\omega$

Fig. 5

The velocity of the modulation will be given by the $\dfrac{dx}{dt}$ in the argument of the cosine term in

equation (19) which is known as the group velocity which in the limiting form is

$$v_g = \dfrac{\Delta\omega}{\Delta k} \rightarrow \dfrac{d\omega}{dk} \qquad \ldots(20)$$

It is the velocity with which the energy of the group is transmitted. Also as $\omega = ck$ we have

$$v_g = c + k\dfrac{dc}{dk} = c - \lambda\dfrac{dc}{d\lambda} \qquad \ldots(21)$$

If the velocity of the wave is independent of the wavelength then $\dfrac{dc}{d\lambda} = 0$ and the group velocity

and the phase velocity is the same. Such a wave is called non-dispersive. However if the wave is

dispersive then $v_g \neq c$ in general.

So far we have confined our attention in this section to travelling (or progressive) wave solutions

of the wave equation. However, it is also possible to have standing waves. This is what takes place in

a sonometer string where a wire with density per unit length ρ and subjected to a tension τ is stretched

between two bridges placed a distance L apart.

In Section 2 of this chapter we derived the wave equation for transverse waves with velocity $c = \sqrt{\tau/\rho}$. Thus the equation governing these transverse vibration is

$$\frac{\partial^2 y}{\partial x^2} = \frac{1}{c^2} \frac{\partial^2 y}{\partial t^2} \qquad \qquad ...(22)$$

but the solutions of physical interest relevant to the sonometer that we search are the ones where y vanishes at the two bridges placed, let us say, at $x = 0$ and $x = L$ at all times since at the two bridges the string in always at rest. The same is the situation for a stringed musical instrument such as the sitar. We look for special solutions which are in fact superposition of left moving and right moving travelling waves with equal amplitude that conspire to keep the displacements at the end points at $x = 0$ and $x = L$ fixed. These are known as normal mode solutions. Let us substitute in the wave-equation the form of the trial solution

$$y(x,t) = \xi(x) \cos (\omega t) \qquad \qquad ...(23)$$

noting that $\dfrac{\partial^2}{\partial t^2} y(x,t) = \xi(x) \dfrac{\partial^2}{\partial t^2} \cos (\omega t) = -\omega^2 \xi(x) \cos \omega t$ the problem reduces to an ordinary differential equation in x, namely

$$\frac{d^2 \xi}{dx^2}(x) = -\frac{\omega^2}{c^2} \xi(x) = -k^2 \xi(x) \qquad \qquad ...(24)$$

where in the last step we have used the relation between the angular frequency ω and the wave number k. This equation is readily tackled to admit solutions sin kx and cos kx. Now $y(x = 0) = 0 = y(x = L)$ are the boundary condition and hence cos kx is not admissible as it does not vanish at $x = 0$. Hence we have $\xi(x) = A \sin kx$ where A is an x (and of course t) independent constant. Having satisfied the boundary condition at $x = 0$ we impose the condition that at $x = L$ ξ must also vanish by demanding that $kL = n\pi$ (where n is an integer viz. 1, 2, 3....).

Thus we arrive at the possible standing wave solutions

$$\xi(x) = A_n \sin \left(\frac{n\pi x}{L} \right) \cos (\omega t) \qquad \qquad ...(25a)$$

with A_n the amplitude of the nth mode (or harmonic) and wave number (k) and wavelength $\left(\lambda = \dfrac{2\pi}{k} \right)$ given by

$$k = \frac{n\pi}{L} \text{ and } \lambda = \frac{2L}{n} \qquad \qquad ...(25b)$$

and angular frequency (ω) and frequency (ν) given by

$$\omega = kc = \frac{n\pi c}{L} \text{ and } \nu = \frac{\omega}{2\pi} = \frac{nc}{2L} = \frac{c}{\lambda} \qquad \qquad ...(25c)$$

These modes of vibration of the string of length L are known as the fundamental ($n = 1$) corresponding to $\lambda = 2L$ and $\nu = \dfrac{c}{2L}$. The others are the harmonics or overtones.

Since we have a linear wave equation, a linear superposition of these solutions is also a solution. Suppose y_1 and y_2 are solutions of the wave equation

$$\frac{\partial^2 y_1}{\partial x^2} = \frac{1}{c^2}\frac{\partial^2 y_1}{\partial t^2} \quad \text{and} \quad \frac{\partial^2 y_2}{\partial x^2} = \frac{1}{c^2}\frac{\partial^2 y_2}{\partial x^2} \qquad \qquad ...(26a)$$

then clearly

$$\frac{\partial^2}{\partial x^2}(a_1 y_1 + a_2 y_2) = \frac{1}{c^2}\frac{\partial^2}{\partial t^2}(a_1 y_1 + a_2 y_2) \qquad \qquad ...(26b)$$

where a_1 and a_2 are constants. This is the very important principle of linear superposition. Thus the most general solution of the vibrating string problem fixed at both ends is

$$y = \sum_n A_n \sin\left(\frac{n\pi x}{L}\right)\cos(\omega t) \qquad \qquad ...(27)$$

To form a clear physical picture of what is going on let us look at the fundamental ($n = 1$) and the first harmonic as shown in the figure below:

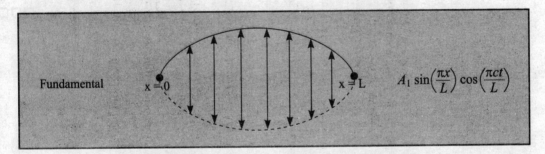

Fundamental $x = 0$ $x = L$ $A_1 \sin\left(\frac{\pi x}{L}\right)\cos\left(\frac{\pi c t}{L}\right)$

Fig. 6

each point on the string is vibrating in time with the amplitudes as shown

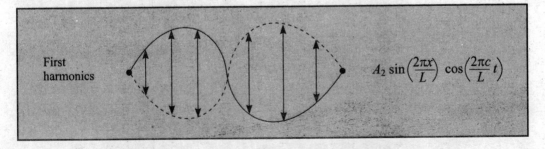

First harmonics $A_2 \sin\left(\frac{2\pi x}{L}\right)\cos\left(\frac{2\pi c}{L}t\right)$

Fig. 7

Furthermore each initial configuration of the string (say the one shown in the figure below correspounding to a plucked string) can be expanded into a Fourier series.

Thus for instance we may express the plucked string at $t = 0$ in a Fourier series in terms of the normal modes as shown below:

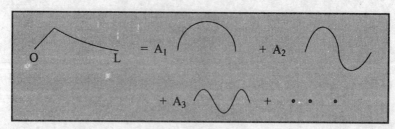

Fig. 8

$$y(x, t = 0) = \sum_{n=1}^{\infty} A_n \sin\left(\frac{n\pi x}{L}\right)$$

At a later time t this will evolve into

$$y(x,t) = \sum_{n=1}^{\infty} A_n \sin\left(\frac{n\pi x}{L}\right) \cos\left(\frac{n\pi ct}{L}\right).$$

□□□

Module Three

Electricity and Magnetism

Scalar and Vector Fields
(Elements of Vector Calculus)

Section 1. SCALAR FIELD GRADIENT

The position or location of a point in three dimensions may be designated by $P(x, y, z)$ or its coordinates in the Cartesian system or by the position vector viz. the vector that joins the origin to the point

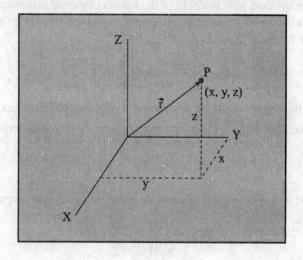

Fig. 1

$$\vec{r} = \hat{i}x + \hat{j}y + \hat{k}z \qquad \qquad ...(1a)$$

where $\hat{i}, \hat{j}, \hat{k}$ are unit vectors along the X, Y, Z axes respectively

The length of the vector is

$$r = |\vec{r}| = \sqrt{x^2 + y^2 + z^2} \qquad \qquad ...(1b)$$

The unit vector in the direction of $\vec{r}$ is

$$\hat{r} = \frac{\vec{r}}{|\vec{r}|} = \frac{\vec{r}}{\sqrt{x^2 + y^2 + z^2}} \qquad \qquad ...(1c)$$

The infinitesimal displacement vector viz. the vector joining P to another point P' with an infinitesimal displacement from it will be written as

$$d\vec{l} = d\vec{r} = \hat{i}dx + \hat{j}dy + \hat{k}dz \qquad \qquad ...(1d)$$

We have already dealt with vectors that change with time, such as the position vector of a point particle $\vec{r}(t)$ and have also used the derivative to define its velocity

$$\frac{d}{dt}\vec{r}(t) = \hat{i}\frac{dx}{dt} + \hat{j}\frac{dy}{dt} + \hat{k}\frac{dz}{dt} \qquad \qquad ...(1e)$$

We go on to define fields starting with the simplest namely the **Scalar field**. This is a scalar quantity which is a function of x, y, z. Examples of scalar fields may be given as temperature values in a given region of space $T(x, y, z)$, density of a non-homogenous medium $\rho(x, y, z)$, the electrostatic potential $\phi(x, y, z)$ etc. We may want to know how a scalar field changes as we move from point to point. For that we would first try to find this change for an infinitesimal displacement. But this question now would also depend on the phrase 'in which direction?'

This question may be addressed with the help of the notion of partial differentiation which enable us to link the infinitesimal change of a function of several variables due to infinitesimal changes in the variables on which the function depends

$$d\phi(x,y,z) = \frac{\partial\phi}{\partial x}dx + \frac{\partial\phi}{\partial y}dy + \frac{\partial\phi}{\partial z}dz \qquad \qquad ...(2a)$$

The above can be conveniently re-expressed using the infinitesimal displacement operator $d\vec{l} = \hat{i}dx + \hat{j}dy + \hat{k}dz$ [see eqn. 1(d)] and by introducing a new 'vector differential operator'.

$$\vec{\nabla} = \hat{i}\frac{\partial}{\partial x} + \hat{j}\frac{\partial}{\partial y} + \hat{k}\frac{\partial}{\partial z} \qquad \qquad ...(2b)$$

which we shall call del or nabla (named after an Assyrian drum of that shape) so that

$$\vec{\nabla}\phi = \hat{i}\frac{\partial\phi}{\partial x} + \hat{j}\frac{\partial\phi}{\partial y} + \hat{k}\frac{\partial\phi}{\partial z} \qquad \qquad ...(2c)$$

One immediately recognises that

$$d\phi = (\vec{\nabla}\phi)\cdot d\vec{l} \qquad \qquad ...(2d)$$

The vector $\vec{\nabla}\phi$ is called the gradient of ϕ. One can also give a geometric interpretation to the gradient of a scalar field. Recalling that the scalar product of two vectors is the product of their magnitudes times the cosine of the angle θ between them we may rewrite eqn. $(2d)$ as

$$d\phi = \left|\vec{\nabla}\phi\right|\left|d\vec{l}\right|\cos\theta \qquad \qquad ...(2e)$$

If for a fixed magnitude $\left|d\vec{l}\right|$ of the displacement we search for the direction in which ϕ changes the most we see that it is $\theta = 0$ or in other words in the direction of the gradient of the scalar field and its magnitude gives us the rate of change.

Section 2. VECTOR FIELD AND ITS DIVERGENCE

Let us consider now a vector field $\vec{V}(x, y, z)$. Examples of such fields are the velocity fields of a fluid in motion, electric or magnetic fields etc.

Consider now the quantity

$$\vec{\nabla} \cdot \vec{V} = \left(\hat{i} \frac{\partial}{\partial x} + \hat{j} \frac{\partial}{\partial y} + \hat{k} \frac{\partial}{\partial z} \right) \cdot \left(\hat{i} V_x + \hat{j} V_y + \hat{k} V_z \right)$$

$$= \frac{\partial}{\partial x} V_x + \frac{\partial}{\partial y} V_y + \frac{\partial}{\partial z} V_z \qquad \qquad \ldots(3)$$

which is called the divergence of the vector field.

The divergence captures an important aspect of the vector field, namely, the 'divergence' of the field in direction or magnitude as the following examples will illustrate. Consider the vector field $V(x, y, z) = \alpha \vec{r}$ where $\alpha =$ constant. A two-dimensional cartoon of this field with $\alpha > 0$ is shown below in Fig. 2a. Though the vector is defind at every point we only show it at two points distant one and two units of length away. Otherwise the figure would have been an undeciferable mess.

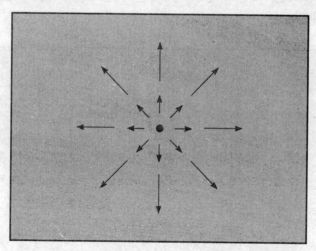

Fig. 2a

Note the positive divergence $\vec{\nabla} \cdot \alpha \vec{r} = \alpha \left(\hat{i} \frac{\partial}{\partial x} + \hat{j} \frac{\partial}{\partial y} + \hat{k} \frac{\partial}{\partial z} \right) \cdot (\hat{i}x + \hat{j}y + \hat{k}z) = 3\alpha$.

If α were negative the arrows would be inward directed. Another rather trivial example would be $\vec{V} = \beta \hat{k}$ with β constant (a uniform field in the z-direction)

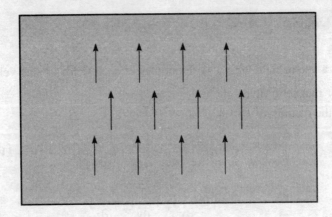

Fig. 2b

Here $\vec{\nabla} \cdot \vec{V} = \left(\hat{i} \dfrac{\partial}{\partial x} + \hat{j} \dfrac{\partial}{\partial y} + \hat{k} \dfrac{\partial}{\partial z} \right) \cdot \beta \hat{k} = \dfrac{\partial}{\partial z} \beta = 0$ there is no divergence in the mathematical as well as the literal sense.

The physical meaning of the divergence of the vector field is best illustrated through the velocity field of a flowing liquid.

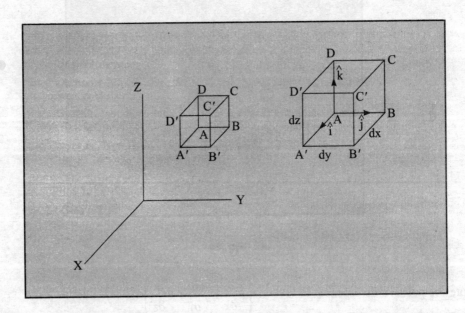

Fig. 3a

Consider a fluid flowing with a velocity field $\vec{v}(x,y,z)$ and in it take a rectangular parallelopiped of infinitesimal dimensions (dx, dy, dz) an exaggerated version of which is shown to the right. Along X-axis passing in through the face *ABCD* (of area *dy dz*) is an amount of fluid per second

$v_x(x,y,z)\, dy\, dz$ as only the normal component of $\vec{v}$ contributes to the flow across that face. At $x + dx$ passing out through the opposite face $A'B'C'D'$ (of area $dy\, dz$) is the amount $v_x(x+dx,y,z)\, dy\, dz =$

$$\left(v_x(x,y,z) + \frac{\partial v_x}{\partial x} dx + .. \right) dy\, dz$$ making a Taylor's expansion. Retaining terms in the Taylor expansion to first order in the infinitesimal dx and subtracting the inflow from the outflow the net outflow due to the x-component of the fluid velocity is given by

$$\frac{\partial v_x}{\partial x}\, dx\, dy\, dz$$

Analogous contributions by the other two pairs of opposite faces gives us the net outflow from the infinitesimal rectangular parallelopiped to be

$$\left(\frac{\partial v_x}{\partial x} + \frac{\partial v_y}{\partial y} + \frac{\partial v_z}{\partial z} \right) dx\, dy\, dz = \vec{\nabla} \cdot \vec{v}\, dx\, dy\, dz \qquad ...(4)$$

If this is positive it means that there must be a source of fluid inside the element while if it is negative a sink is indicated. Thus the divergence is a measure of the source strength.

The result may be extended to a finite volume V bounded by a closed surface S. Subdivide the region into volume elements as shown in Fig. 3(b). The sizes of these elements have been exaggerated for the sake of clarity.

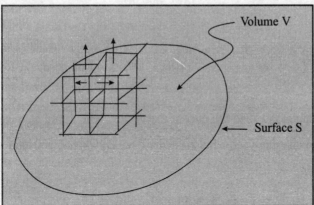

Fig. 3b Gauss's Theorem

The meaning of the divergence of the vector $\vec{v}$ holds in each of the elements. But note that each interior surface element occurs twice as we sum over all the rectangular parallelopipeds. What flows out of a face from one cube enters the next. The loss in one is the gain in the other and as we add up all the contribution the net flow through the internal faces all cancel. The only survivors are the faces of the elements of the surface S. In the limit with elements becoming smaller the sum becomes the integral over the volume of the divergence and the outflow the surface integral of the normal to the surface $\vec{v} \cdot d\vec{S}$ and so we have what is known as the Gauss's Theorem (or the Divergence Theorem)

$$\oint_s \vec{v} \cdot d\vec{S} = \int_v \vec{\nabla} \cdot \vec{v}\, dV \qquad ...(5)$$

The surface integral of the normal component of a vector field $\vec{v}$ taken over a closed surface S (closed indicated by the circle on the integral sign) is equal to the volume integral of the divergence of $\vec{v}$ taken over the enclosed volume.

Section 3. THE CURL OF A VECTOR FIELD

Using the vector operator $\vec{\nabla}$ or nabla we have seen how we can obtain a vector field from a scalar field through the gradient operation $\vec{\nabla}\phi$, and a scalar field from a vector field through the divergence operation $\vec{\nabla} \cdot \vec{v}$, and have also appreciated the usefulness and physical meaning of these operations. We now go on to discuss how we can obtain a vector from a vector field and its physical meaning.

Consider a vector field $\vec{v} = \vec{v}(x, y, z)$ and carry out the operation $\vec{\nabla} \times \vec{v}$ which is the vector (or cross) product of the vector operator $\vec{\nabla} = \hat{i}\dfrac{\partial}{\partial x} + \hat{j}\dfrac{\partial}{\partial y} + \hat{k}\dfrac{\partial}{\partial z}$ and the $\vec{v} = \hat{i}v_x + \hat{j}v_y + \hat{k}v_z$ and hence given by

$$\vec{\nabla} \times \vec{v} = \begin{vmatrix} \hat{i} & \hat{j} & \hat{k} \\ \dfrac{\partial}{\partial x} & \dfrac{\partial}{\partial y} & \dfrac{\partial}{\partial z} \\ v_x & v_y & v_z \end{vmatrix}$$

$$= \hat{i}\left(\frac{\partial v_z}{\partial y} - \frac{\partial v_y}{\partial z}\right) + \hat{j}\left(\frac{\partial v_x}{\partial z} - \frac{\partial v_z}{\partial x}\right) + \hat{k}\left(\frac{\partial v_y}{\partial x} - \frac{\partial v_x}{\partial y}\right) \qquad \ldots(6)$$

The vector so obtained is called the curl of the vector field $\vec{v}$, and also called the circulation.

Let us for instance take the vector field $\vec{v} = \vec{\omega} \times \vec{r}$ where $\vec{\omega}$ is a constant vector

$$\vec{v} = \vec{\omega} \times \vec{r} = \begin{vmatrix} \hat{i} & \hat{j} & \hat{k} \\ \omega_1 & \omega_2 & \omega_3 \\ x & y & z \end{vmatrix}$$

$$= \hat{i}(\omega_2 z - \omega_3 y) + \hat{j}(\omega_3 x - \omega_1 z) + \hat{k}(\omega_1 y - \omega_2 x)$$

$$\vec{\nabla} \times \vec{v} = \begin{vmatrix} \hat{i} & \hat{j} & \hat{k} \\ \dfrac{\partial}{\partial x} & \dfrac{\partial}{\partial y} & \dfrac{\partial}{\partial z} \\ \omega_2 z - \omega_3 y & \omega_3 x - \omega_1 z & \omega_1 y - \omega_2 x \end{vmatrix}$$

$$= \hat{i}2\omega_1 + \hat{j}2\omega_2 + \hat{k}2\omega_3 = 2\vec{\omega}$$

Taking ω to be along the Z-axis we can plot the vector field in the *XY*-plane as shown in Fig. 4.

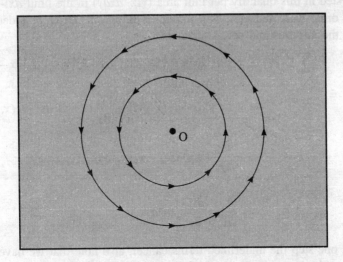

Fig. 4

Indeed if we were to rotate this sheet of paper about an axis perpendicular to this plane passing through *O* with an angular velocity ω (along *z*) each point would trace out a circle as shown. The tangents at each point would give the direction of the velocity and the speed would be *r*ω in magnitude. The $\bar{v}(x,y)$ would constitute a vector field. The circles may be called field lines. As one can see the vector $\bar{v}$ **curls** around *O*. The velocity field of a fluid rotating about a circular obstacle has a similar appearance. Another example would be the magnetic field due to an electric current flowing through a wire at right angles to the plane.

The meaning of the curl of a vector field is further sharpened by considering a vector field $\bar{v}(x,y,z)$ and choosing a small rectangular area say in the *XY*-plane.

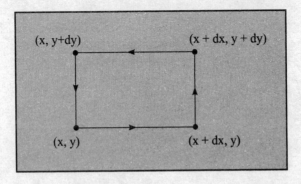

Fig. 5a

Let us compute $\int \vec{v} \cdot d\vec{l}$ viz. the line integral for this infinitesimal element of area. Since we shall ultimately be interested in this quantity per unit area (viz. $dxdy$) in the limit $dx \to 0$ and $dy \to 0$ we shall keep terms of order $dxdy$ and may with impunity throw out terms of order $(dx)^2$ or $(dy)^2$. The line "integral" over the infinitesimal perimeter is thus

$$\sum \vec{v} \cdot d\vec{l} = v_x(x,y)dx + v_y(x+dx,y)dy - v_x(x,y+dy)dx - v_y(x,y)dy$$

$$= \underline{v_x(x,y)dx} + \underline{v_y(x,y)dy} + \frac{\partial v_y}{\partial x}(x,y)dxdy - \underline{v_x(x,y)dx}$$

$$- \frac{\partial v_x}{\partial y}(x,y)dxdy - \underline{v_y(x,y)dy}$$

$$= \left(\frac{\partial v_y}{\partial x} - \frac{\partial v_x}{\partial y}\right)dx\,dy$$

In the last but one step the underlined terms cancel, also note that we have not kept $(dx)^2$ and $(dy)^2$ terms as they are irrelevent in the limit of small dx and dy.

Noting that in this case the element of area is $dx\,dy\,\hat{k} = d\vec{S}$ and that $\frac{\partial v_y}{\partial x} - \frac{\partial v_x}{\partial y} = (\vec{\nabla} \times \vec{v})_z$, we have obtained for the infinitesimal closed line integral the result that $\oint \vec{v} \cdot d\vec{l} = \int (\vec{\nabla} \times \vec{v}) \cdot d\vec{S}$. If we had chosen any other plane clearly the analogous result would have followed.

Just as in the case of the Gauss' Theorem we may consider a portion of a surface S (not necessarily on a plane) bounded by a closed curve C.

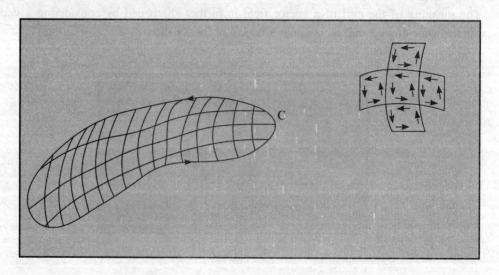

Fig. 5 b

If the surface be subdivided into infinitesimally small elements the contributions to the line integral from the inner dividing lines cancel out as each segment is traversed twice in opposite directions. The line segments which are left uncancelled are merely those along the bounding curve C.

And hence we have the Stokes's Theorem

$$\oint_c \vec{v} \cdot d\vec{l} = \int (\vec{\nabla} \times \vec{v}) \cdot d\vec{S} \qquad ...(7)$$

or the line integral of the vector field $\vec{v}$ taken over a closed curve C is equal to the surface integral of the curl of $\vec{v}$ taken over any surface having curve C as a boundary.

Later in our study of electrostatics and magnetism we shall see the immense power of the theorems due to Gauss and that due to Stokes.

Section 4. CONSERVATIVE OR GRADIENT FIELDS

Gradient fields are vector fields that can be derived from a scalar function $\phi(x,y,z)$ as the negative gradient of ϕ (known as the potential)

$$\vec{v} = -\vec{\nabla}\phi$$

Note that for such a vector field the line integral from some point A to B along some path P.

$$I = \int_A^B \vec{v} \cdot d\vec{l}$$

(along *APB*)

$$= -\int_A^B \vec{\nabla}\phi \cdot d\vec{l} = -\int_A^B \left(\hat{i}\frac{\partial\phi}{\partial x} + \hat{j}\frac{\partial\phi}{\partial y} + \hat{k}\frac{\partial\phi}{\partial z} \right)(\hat{i}dx + \hat{j}dy + \hat{k}dz)$$

$$= -\int_A^B \left(\frac{\partial\phi}{\partial x}dx + \frac{\partial\phi}{\partial y}dy + \frac{\partial\phi}{\partial z}dz \right)$$

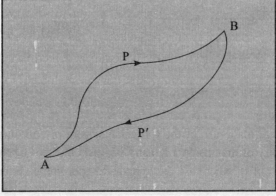

Fig. 6

Noting that the integrand is a total derivative

$$I = -\int_A^B \frac{d\phi}{dl}\, dl = -(\phi_B - \phi_A) \qquad ...(8)$$

It only depends on the values of potential ϕ at the endpoints A and B and **not** on the path taken. Put another way consider the integral

$$I' = \int_{BP'A} \vec{v}.\vec{dl} = -(\phi_A - \phi_B) = -I$$

and therefore $I + I' = 0$ or in other words for such a gradient vector field

$$\oint \vec{v}.\vec{dl} = 0$$

the line integral over any closed curve is zero.

Another property of such gradient fields is revealed when we consider their curl

$$\vec{\nabla} \times \vec{v} = \left(\hat{i}\frac{\partial}{\partial x} + \hat{j}\frac{\partial}{\partial y} + \hat{k}\frac{\partial}{\partial z} \right) \times \left(\hat{i}\frac{\partial \phi}{\partial x} + \hat{j}\frac{\partial \phi}{\partial y} + \hat{k}\frac{\partial \phi}{\partial z} \right) = 0 \qquad ...(9)$$

as

$$\frac{\partial^2 \phi}{\partial y \partial x} = \frac{\partial^2 \phi}{\partial x \partial y}\ \text{etc.}$$

Thus the curl of a gradient field vanishes.

We have already seen that the divergence of a vector field is an important quantity as it tells us about sources. When the vector field is a gradient field in that case we have

$$\vec{\nabla} \cdot \vec{v} = \vec{\nabla} \cdot \vec{\nabla}\phi = \left(\hat{i}\frac{\partial}{\partial x} + \hat{j}\frac{\partial}{\partial y} + \hat{k}\frac{\partial}{\partial z} \right) \cdot \left(\hat{i}\frac{\partial \phi}{\partial x} + \hat{j}\frac{\partial \phi}{\partial y} + \hat{k}\frac{\partial \phi}{\partial z} \right)$$

$$= \frac{\partial^2 \phi}{\partial x^2} + \frac{\partial^2 \phi}{\partial y^2} + \frac{\partial^2 \phi}{\partial z^2} \equiv \nabla^2 \phi \qquad ...(10)$$

In the last step we have define an operator $\nabla^2 = \vec{\nabla} \cdot \vec{\nabla} = \dfrac{\partial^2}{\partial x^2} + \dfrac{\partial^2}{\partial y^2} + \dfrac{\partial^2}{\partial z^2}$ which occurs very often

in physics and is known as the Laplacian.

Section 5. CURVILINEAR COORDINATES

So far we have by and large made use of the Cartesian system of coordinates in our considerations. However often the symmetry of the problem at hand suggests the use of other coordinates such as for instance the spherical polar or in other case the cylindrical coordinate system.

Spherical Polar Coordinates

The spherical polar coordinates (r, θ, ϕ) of a point P are shown in Fig. 7 defined as follows:

r is the distance of the point P from the origin O.

θ is the angle made by OP with the z-axis. Identifying the z-axis as the polar axis of the earth in geographical terms θ is the co-lattitude (or the complement of the lattitude of the point P). θ is also called the polar angle of the point P.

ϕ is the angle around from the x-axis or the azimuthal angle. In geographical terms identifying the XY-plane as the plane of the equation and the line of longitude joining through a great circle the north and south poles passing through the point where the X-axis pierces this our 'earthly sphare' as the Greenwich meridian (0° longitude), the azimuthal angle ϕ is the longitude of the point P.

Refer to Fig. 7 to realise that the ranges of the coordinate r is $0 \le r < \infty$, while $0 \le \theta \le \pi$ and $0 \le \phi \le 2\pi$ unlike what one has in the Cartesian system $-\infty \le x, y, z \le +\infty$ as our coordinates must cover the whole of space once and only once.

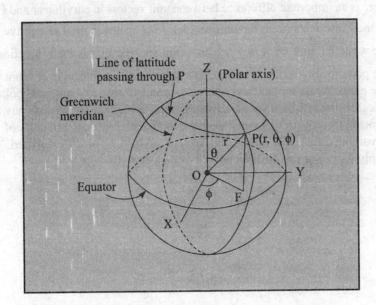

Fig. 7

To relate the Cartesian coordinates to the spherical polar we note that the distance OF (F being the foot of the perpendicular dropped from the point P on the equatorial plane) is simply $r \sin \theta$ and the x and y coordinate are just the perpendicular distances to the X and Y axes respectively, we get

$$x = r \sin \theta \cos \phi, \qquad y = r \sin \theta \sin \phi, \qquad z = r \cos \theta \qquad \text{...(11)}$$

and conversely

$$r = \sqrt{x^2 + y^2 + z^2}, \quad \theta = \tan^{-1}\left(\frac{\sqrt{x^2 + y^2}}{z}\right), \qquad \phi = \tan^{-1}\left(\frac{y}{x}\right) \qquad \text{...(12)}$$

We can also define three unit vectors appropriate to this system of coordinates, namely $\hat{r}$ in the radial direction (that of increasing r), $\hat{\theta}$ unit vector tangential to the great circle of longitude passing through P, in the direction of increasing θ, $\hat{\phi}$ unit vector tangential to the line of lattitude passing through P and in the direction of increasing ϕ.

Any vector $\bar{v}$ can be expressed in terms of these three unit vectors which are also orthogonal to each other viz. $\hat{r}.\hat{\theta} = \hat{r} \cdot \hat{\phi} = \hat{\theta} \cdot \hat{\phi} = 0$

$$\bar{v} = v_r\hat{r} + v_\theta\hat{\theta} + v_\phi\hat{\phi} \qquad \text{...(13)}$$

and v_r, v_θ, v_ϕ are the radial, polar and azimuthal components of the vector $\bar{v}$. These unit vectors can readily be expressed in terms of the unit vectors $\hat{i}, \hat{j}, \hat{k}$ of the Cartesian system

$$\hat{r} = \sin\theta\cos\phi\hat{i} + \sin\theta\sin\phi\hat{j} + \cos\theta\hat{k} \qquad \text{...(13a)}$$

$$\hat{\theta} = \cos\theta\cos\phi\hat{i} + \cos\theta\sin\phi\hat{j} - \sin\theta\hat{k} \qquad \text{...(13b)}$$

$$\hat{\phi} = -\sin\phi\hat{i} + \cos\phi\hat{j} \qquad \text{...(13c)}$$

However there is an important difference between unit vectors in curvilinear and Cartesian system of coordinates. In the Cartesian system the unit vectors $\hat{i}, \hat{j}, \hat{k}$ point in their respective fixed directions where ever we are while the unit vectors $\hat{r}, \hat{\theta}, \hat{\phi}$ are point specific that is their directions change when we move from one point to another. For example, the unit vector $\hat{r}$ points to every spot in the sky as we wander all over the earth. While we have everything to gain by using say spherical polar coordinates in describing a physical situation where we do have spherical symmetry we have to pay a little price for the simplification made thereby, in that when we have to take divergences and curls of vectors or carry out any process involving differentiation the unit vectors too have to be differentiated. Thus refering to eqns. (13) we simply carry out the differentiations to deduce that

$$\frac{\partial\hat{r}}{\partial\theta} = \hat{\theta}, \quad \frac{\partial\hat{r}}{\partial\phi} = \sin\theta\hat{\phi}, \quad \frac{\partial\hat{r}}{\partial r} = 0 \qquad \text{...(14a)}$$

$$\frac{\partial\hat{\theta}}{\partial\theta} = -\hat{r}, \quad \frac{\partial\hat{\theta}}{\partial\phi} = \cos\theta\hat{\phi}, \quad \frac{\partial\hat{\theta}}{\partial r} = 0 \qquad \text{...(14b)}$$

$$\frac{\partial\hat{\phi}}{\partial\theta} = 0, \quad \frac{\partial\hat{\phi}}{\partial\phi} = -\sin\theta\hat{r} - \cos\theta\hat{\theta}, \quad \frac{\partial\hat{\phi}}{\partial r} = 0 \qquad \text{...(14c)}$$

We may also need the infinitesimal displacement vector $d\bar{l}$ which was simply $\hat{i}dx + \hat{j}dy + \hat{k}dz$ in the Cartesian system. In the spherical polar coordinate system we can readily see that while in the direction $\hat{r}$ this is simply dr, in the direction $\hat{\theta}$ the component of $d\bar{l}$ is the arc length $rd\theta$ along the line of longitude as evident from Fig. 7; and similarly in the direction $\hat{\phi}$ it is the arc length along the line of lattitude (a circle of radius $r\sin\theta$) which is $r\sin\theta\,d\phi$ and thus

$$d\bar{l} = \hat{r}dr + \hat{\theta}rd\theta + \hat{\phi}r\sin\theta d\phi \qquad \text{...(15)}$$

This we shall need when confronted with a line integral.

The element of volume is just like in the Cartesian system $dV = dx\, dy\, dz$, here too the product of the line elements in the three orthogonal directions $\hat{r}, \hat{\theta}, \hat{\phi}$ and we have

$$dV = (dr)(rd\theta)(r\sin\theta d\phi) = r^2 \sin\theta dr d\theta d\phi \qquad \ldots(16)$$

Turning out attention to vector calculus in curvilinear coordinates let us first look at the gradient of a scalar field $S(\vec{r}) = S(z, y, z)$ viz. $\vec{\nabla} S = \hat{i}\dfrac{\partial S}{\partial x} + \hat{j}\dfrac{\partial S}{\partial y} + \hat{k}\dfrac{\partial S}{\partial z}$. One could now simply use the chain rule for differentiation to write

$$\frac{\partial S}{\partial x} = \frac{\partial S}{\partial r}\frac{\partial r}{\partial x} + \frac{\partial S}{\partial \theta}\frac{\partial \theta}{\partial x} + \frac{\partial S}{\partial \phi}\frac{\partial \phi}{\partial x}$$

and then as $r = \sqrt{x^2 + y^2 + z^2}$ we have $\dfrac{\partial r}{\partial x} = \dfrac{x}{r}$ and as $\theta = \tan^{-1}\left(\dfrac{\sqrt{x^2 + y^2}}{z}\right)$ we have

$$\frac{\partial \theta}{\partial x} = \frac{1}{1 + \left(\dfrac{\sqrt{x^2 + y^2}}{z}\right)^2} \cdot \frac{x}{z}\frac{1}{\sqrt{x^2 + y^2}} = \frac{\cos\theta\cos\phi}{r};$$ and as $\phi = \tan^{-1}\left(\dfrac{y}{x}\right)$ we have $\dfrac{\partial \phi}{\partial x} = -\dfrac{1}{r}\dfrac{\sin\phi}{\sin\theta}$. This

painful process has to be carried out for $\dfrac{\partial S}{\partial y}$ and $\dfrac{\partial S}{\partial z}$, so that now $\vec{\nabla} S$ is re-expressed from $\dfrac{\partial S}{\partial x}, \dfrac{\partial S}{\partial y}, \dfrac{\partial S}{\partial z}$

to $\dfrac{\partial S}{\partial r}, \dfrac{\partial S}{\partial \theta}, \dfrac{\partial S}{\partial \phi}$. Next we use equations (13) to translate the expression from $\hat{i}, \hat{j}, \hat{k}$ to $\hat{r}, \hat{\theta}, \hat{\phi}$ and this leads after a considerable amount of straight forward labour to arrive at the result

$$\vec{\nabla} S = \frac{\partial S}{\partial r}\hat{r} + \frac{1}{r}\frac{\partial S}{\partial \theta}\hat{\theta} + \frac{1}{r\sin\theta}\frac{\partial S}{\partial \phi}\hat{\phi} \qquad \ldots(17)$$

Again through hard work one obtains

$$\nabla^2 S = \frac{1}{r^2}\frac{\partial}{\partial r}\left(r^2\frac{\partial S}{\partial r}\right) + \frac{1}{r^2 \sin\theta}\frac{\partial}{\partial \theta}\left(\sin\theta\frac{\partial}{\partial \theta}\right)S + \frac{1}{r^2 \sin^2\theta}\frac{\partial^2}{\partial \phi^2}S \qquad \ldots(18)$$

Proceeding similarly one could also translate the divergence and curl of a vector but now in addition one must be cautious that the unit vectors in a curvilinear system are position dependent [see eqns. 14] and arrive at

$$\vec{\nabla} \cdot \vec{v} = \frac{1}{r^2}\frac{\partial}{\partial r}(r^2 v_r) + \frac{1}{r\sin\theta}\frac{\partial}{\partial \theta}(\sin\theta v_\theta) + \frac{1}{r\sin\theta}\frac{\partial v_\phi}{\partial \phi} \qquad \ldots(19)$$

and
$$\vec{\nabla} \times \vec{v} = \frac{1}{r \sin\theta} \left[\frac{\partial}{\partial\theta}(\sin\theta\, v_\phi) - \frac{\partial v_\theta}{\partial\phi} \right]\hat{r} + \frac{1}{r}\left[\frac{1}{\sin\theta}\frac{\partial v_r}{\partial\phi} - \frac{\partial}{\partial r}(rv_\phi) \right]\hat{\theta} + \frac{1}{r}\left[\frac{\partial}{\partial r}(rv_\theta) - \frac{\partial v_r}{\partial\theta} \right]\hat{\phi} \quad ...(20)$$

Cylindrical coordinate system

In problems which possess axial symmetry (there is an axis of symmetry, rotation about which, keeps the physics unchanged, such as for a solenoid) it is advantageous to use the cylindrical coordinates.

In this coordinate system (ρ, ϕ, z) define the location of a point P as shown in Fig. 8.

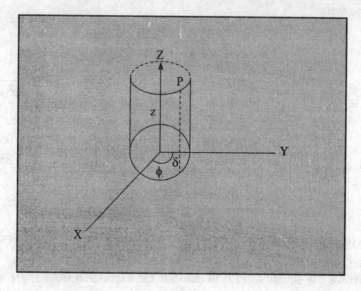

Fig. 8

The point P lies on a cylinder of radius ρ with its axis along the Z-axis. The range of the variables are clearly $-\infty \le z \le +\infty, 0 \le \rho \le \infty, 0 \le \phi \le 2\pi$.

Clearly

$$x = \rho \cos\phi \qquad y = \rho \sin\phi \qquad z = z \qquad ...(21)$$

The unit vectors $\hat{\rho}$ along the direction of increasing ρ (outward drawn normal to the cylinder at a point of given ϕ is obviously

$$\hat{\rho} = \hat{i} \cos\phi + \hat{j}\sin\phi \qquad ...(22a)$$

and $\hat{\phi}$ along the direction of increasing ϕ the tangent to the circle shown in the figure

$$\hat{\phi} = -\hat{i}\sin\phi + \hat{j}\cos\phi \qquad ...(22b)$$

and of course the direction of increasing z

$$\hat{z} = \hat{k} \qquad ...(22c)$$

The line element, which is

$$d\vec{l} = \hat{\rho}d\rho + \hat{\phi}\rho d\phi + \hat{z}dz \qquad \ldots(23)$$

and the volume element

$$dV = \rho d\rho\, d\phi\, dz \qquad \ldots(24)$$

are easily worked out.

The expressions for the gradient divergence curl and Laplacian which can be painstakingly but straight-forwardly worked out are given by

$$\vec{\nabla}S = \frac{\partial S}{\partial \rho}\hat{\rho} + \frac{1}{\rho}\frac{\partial S}{\partial \phi}\hat{\phi} + \frac{\partial S}{\partial z}\hat{z} \qquad \ldots(25)$$

$$\vec{\nabla} \cdot \vec{v} = \frac{1}{\rho}\frac{\partial}{\partial \rho}(\rho v_\rho) + \frac{1}{\rho}\frac{\partial v_\phi}{\partial \phi} + \frac{\partial v_z}{\partial z} \qquad \ldots(26)$$

$$\vec{\nabla} \times \vec{v} = \left(\frac{1}{\rho}\frac{\partial v_z}{\partial \phi} - \frac{\partial v_\phi}{\partial z}\right)\hat{\rho} + \left(\frac{\partial v_\rho}{\partial z} - \frac{\partial v_z}{\partial \rho}\right)\hat{\phi}$$

$$+ \frac{1}{\rho}\left(\frac{\partial}{\partial \rho}(\rho v_\phi) - \frac{\partial v_\rho}{\partial \phi}\right)\hat{z} \qquad \ldots(27)$$

$$\nabla^2 S = \frac{1}{\rho}\frac{\partial}{\partial \rho}\left(\rho \frac{\partial S}{\partial \rho}\right) + \frac{1}{\rho^2}\frac{\partial^2 S}{\partial \phi^2} + \frac{\partial^2 S}{\partial z^2} \qquad \ldots(28)$$

□□□

6

Electrostatics

Electrostatic phenomena were known since ancient times, when it was found that some substances when rubbed by others [such as amber (petrified resin) rubbed with straw] would attract small pieces of straw. Thanks to developments over the centuries we now know that matter consisting of neutral atoms (and molecules) which consist of electrons (carrying negative charge) that are bound to the positively charged nuclei and that some substances have greater electron affinity and rubbing causes transfer of some of the electrons from the substance of lesser affinity making the latter positively charged. Indeed the Greek word for amber was ελεκτρον to which our electron owes its name. Not until the 17th century did Sir William Gilbert physician in the court of Queen Elizabeth I of England not only classified substances with this interesting (but at that time totally mysterious) property, but also devised some instruments to collect these "charges", which they thought were two kinds of fluids existing in substances. The same Gilbert also systematized and further developed what was known till that time on magnetism (indeed the very word is derived from the Greek name of Magnesia a region in Asia Minor, present day Turkey, where magnetic rocks were found; the lodestone or north seeking mineral rock was known even earlier to the Chinese).

It was Charles Augustin de Coulomb (1736 – 1806) who published the first quantitative results (and formulated the basic law) through his papers on electric charges between 1785 – 1789. He found that there were two types of charge (positive and negative). Like charges repel and unlike charges attract. He had invented a torsion balance with the help of which he could measure the attraction or repulsion of two electrically charged spheres. On the basis of extensive experimentation he was able to arrive at the conclusion that in electric attraction or repulsion the force is proportional to the product of the two charges and inversely proportional to the square of the distance between the two charges (*viz.* the centres of the spheres). It is therefore appropriate that we start with electrostatics charges *per se* but not in movement.

The next important step at a conceptual sequence of events was taken by **Luigi Galvani** (1737 – 1798) who discovered accidently that a continuous flow of electrical current (charge flow) could be induced by bringing two dissimilar metals (in his case iron and copper) into contact with a moist substance in between. Although he did not understand the principle, his pioneering experiments inspired further developments. He used, as a physiologist, the twitching of a dissected frog's leg muscles as a kind of "current meter". Yet Galvani was somewhat confused between cause and effect, which is even evident in the title of his short conclusive article entitled "Commentary on the Forces of

Electricity in Muscular Motion". As a part of this important development and clarification of the basics stands the name of Alessandro Volta (1745 – 1827) after whom the unit of electromotive force, the Volt is named. It was this child born near the Lake Como in Italy, who only learnt to speak his first words at the age of four years, who developed the theory of the electric current and invented the first electric battery. In 1800 Volta succeeded in generating electricity by connecting two bowls of salt solution with a metal arc, one end of which was copper and the other tin or zinc. The same year he also constructed the voltaic pile, the first battery of cells (alternating disks of copper, cardboard soaked in salt-water and zinc). It was Georg Simon Ohm (1787 – 1854) who connected the poles of a battery of cells through various wires and observed that such wires built of different materials are differently heated by the current. He observed the regularities and to him we owe the connection between the electromotive force generated by the battery of cells and the current (charge per second) flowing through the conducter (which is known as Ohm's Law and introduced the notion of resistance of a wire and the resistivity of the material out of which it is made). These discoveries were made in the decade of the twenties of the nineteenth century. Hence it is appropriate that Chapter 7 be devoted to Current Electricity.

The Danish scientist Hans Christian Oersted (1777 – 1851) made a discovery in 1819 while conducting a demonstration for students during a lecture. He noticed that when a magnetic compass was brought near a current carrying wire the needle was deflected. In a matter of days after hearing of this discovery André Marié Ampére (1775 – 1836) formulated the theoretical basis for this phenomenon of electromagnetism, and by asserting that a current loop carrying an electric current I and having an area. A has a **magnetic moment** proportional to the product IA, and in the direction perpendicular to the plane of the loop laid the foundation of the relationship between electricity and magnetism.

Furthermore the force between two current carrying elements (($d\vec{l}_1$ and $d\vec{l}_2$) with currents I_1 and I_2)

separated by the vector $\vec{r}$ was found to be proportional to $I_1 I_2 \dfrac{d\vec{l}_2 \times (d\vec{l}_1 \times \hat{r})}{r^2}$, again the inverse square

law (This is also often called the Biot-Savart Law). The Coulomb's Law of force between charges and the Biot-Savart Law of force between current carrying elements (both depending inversely on the square of the distance between them) suggested that electromagnetism would also develop along the lines of Newton's work on gravitational interaction in terms of action at a distance.

However this was **not** to be! Indeed Newton himself was extremely suspicious of his own idea of instantaneous action at a distance. In his own words: "That one body may act upon another at a distance through a vacuum without the mediation of anything else .... is to me so great an absurdity that no man, who has in philosophic matters a competent faculty of thinking, can ever fall into it". It was Michael Faraday, who in the first half of the nineteenth century gave a central role to fields in the theory of electromagnetism. The reduction of the Coulomb force (if the medium between two charged bodies is a dielectric) led Faraday to emphasize that the atoms or molecules of the medium were polarised and the consequent bound charge separation contributed to the electric field and modified it. He described the effect through lines of force in the region between the charges. His discovery of electromagnetic induction in which an electromotive force was generated by the time rate of charge of the magnetic flux through the circuit convinced him of the tangible reality of the magnetic field and its flux. But Faraday coming as he did from a working-class background with little formal education was not sufficiently equipped with mathematics and his contemporary Gauss furnished the first mathematical formulation of the underlying field theory. In the present textbook Chapter 8 is thus devoted to Magnetic Effect of Currents and Electromagnetic Induction.

Some thirty years after Faraday's early discoveries Maxwell armed with the findings and deep insight of Faraday and the work of Gauss and the mathematical contributions of Laplace, Poisson and Green (some of these work being concerned with the introduction of potential in gravitation theory) went about systematically in developing the theory of electric and magnetic fields (considered as physical entities and not merely as mathematical devices). He also introduced the notion of the displacement current which also proved to be essential to have a mathematically consistent theory. And was even more dramatic, he was able to predict on the basis of his equations (which accounted for all the known physics and observations involving electric charges and currents and magnets and their interactions) a new phenomenon. That a periodic oscillation of an electric current source would travel out as a wave in the electric and magnetic fields that would travel with a speed (predicted correctly) which was that of light. Thus at one fell stroke Maxwell was able not only to establish the physical reality of fields but also to unify two great areas of physics — electromagnetism and optics. This will be described in Chapter 9.

Section 1. COULOMB'S LAW AND THE ELECTRIC FIELD

On the basis of painstaking experiments using his torsion balance measuring the force between electrostatically charged pith-balls Coulomb in 1785 published his finding in the statement that the force between two charges say q and Q is proportional to the product of the charges and inversely to the square of the distance between them and is directed along the line joining them; it is attractive if the two charges are unlike (q, Q have opposite signs) and repulsive if they are like (q, Q have the same sign).

Before discussing the constant of proportionality we must state what is the quantitative measure of this "electric charge". This is linked to the system of units that we use.

One of these systems is the C.G.S. Gaussian system. In this system the unit of length is the **centimetre**, that of mass is the **gram** and that of time is the **second**. In this system the unit of force is the **dyne** which is the force which when acting on a mass of one gram causes an acceleration of 1 cm/sec^2. The unit of energy is the **erg** that is the work done in moving 1 cm against a force of 1 dyne. In this system the unit of charge is called a **stat-coulomb**. This is a charge which when placed 1 cm away from an identical such charge feels a force of repulsion of 1 dyne. This in the C.G.S. Gaussian electrostatic (esu) units the Coulomb's Law reads

$$\vec{F} = \frac{qQ}{r^2}\hat{r} \qquad \qquad ...(1a)$$

where $\hat{r}$ is the unit vector along the line joining the two. This system of units is used by those who work on the physics of atoms, nuclei, solids and elementary particles.

However from a more everyday point of view an international system of units was established in 1960 called SI system of units (Système International in French) which is also called rationalized MKSA system. The word rationalized means that certain factors of 4π are put in at the level of basic laws such that they do not appear in more applied situations. MKSA means metre, kilogram, second, ampere. Here the unit of length is the metre, that of mass is the kilogram, of time the second. Force in this system is measured in Newtons (abbreviated N) which is the force which when acting on a particle of mass one kilogram causes on acceleration of 1 m/s^2 (metre per second squared). The unit of energy is a Joule (abbreviated J) which is the work done against a Newton of force with a displacement of one metre. The unit of charge here is, however, defined in terms of the current which is the flow of charge (this we shall discuss in the next chapter). The ampere is the unit of current which will then be defined. A Coulomb is the quantity of charge transported in one second by a current of one ampere. (This will become clearer after the next chapter).

These apart one defines two quantities.

ε_0 = permittivity of vacuum = 8.85×10^{-12} C^2/Nm^2

μ_0 = permeability of vacuum = $4\pi \times 10^{-7}$ N/A^2.

So that $\dfrac{1}{4\pi}\varepsilon_0 \approx 9\times10^9$ N $\cdot$ m^2/C^2 (a value we shall use in out text)

In the SI units the Coulomb's Law reads

$$\vec{F} = \frac{1}{4\pi\varepsilon_0}\frac{qQ}{r^2}\hat{r} \qquad \qquad ...(1b)$$

here q and Q are to be expressed not in terms of stat-coulombs but in terms of Coulombs.

Thus, for instance the magnitude of the force $\left|\vec{F}\right|$ between two charges $q = Q = 1C$ (Coulomb) separated by a distance $r = 1$ m (metre) is readily calculated

$$\left|\vec{F}\right| = \frac{1}{4\pi\varepsilon_0}\cdot\frac{qQ}{r^2} = 9\times10^9\,\frac{\text{N}\cdot\text{m}^2}{\text{C}^2}\cdot\frac{\text{C}\times\text{C}}{(1\text{m})^2} = 9\times10^9\,\text{N}$$

For the sake of comparison the gravitational force between two masses of 1 kg each separated by a distance of 1 metre is given by

$$\left|\vec{F}\right| = G\frac{mM}{r^2} = 6\cdot7\times10^{-11}\left(\frac{\text{N}\cdot\text{m}^2}{(\text{kg})^2}\right)\cdot\frac{1\text{kg}\times1\text{kg}}{(1\text{ m})^2}$$

$$= 6.7 \times 10^{-11}\,\text{N}$$

as $$G = 6\cdot7\times10^{-11}\,\frac{\text{N}\cdot\text{m}^2}{(\text{kg})^2}$$

As another illustration consider the force between an electron and a proton separated by a distance of 1 Å = 10^{-10} m. The charge of the electron is -1.6×10^{-19}C and so is that of the proton (though of opposite sign) hence the Coulomb force between them is in magnitude

$$\left|\vec{F}\right| = 9\times10^9\,\frac{\text{N}\cdot\text{m}^2}{\text{C}^2}\frac{1\cdot6\times10^{-19}\text{C}\times1\cdot6\times10^{-19}\text{C}}{(10^{-10}\text{ m})^2}$$

$$\approx 2\cdot3\times10^{-8}\,\text{N}$$

while the magnitude of the gravitational force is

$$|\vec{F}| = 6.7 \times 10^{-11} \frac{N \cdot m^2}{(kg)^2} \cdot \frac{9 \times 10^{-31} kg \times 1 \cdot 67 \times 10^{-27} kg}{(10^{-10} m)^2}$$

$$\approx 10^{-47} N$$

It is worthwhile calculating the magnitude of the Coulomb force is Gaussian C.G.S. units (because atomic scientists often work in this system). In these units the magnitude of the charge on the electron (or proton) is 4.8×10^{-10} stat-coulomb which is the e.s.u. (or electrostatic unit) unit of charge. Indeed $1 C = 3 \times 10^9$ stat-coulombs. The unit of distance is a centimetre (cm) and hence $1 \text{Å} = 10^{-8}$ cm. The force law here being $\vec{F} = \frac{qQ}{r^2} \hat{r}$ we have

$$|\vec{F}| = \frac{4.8 \times 10^{-10} \times 4.8 \times 10^{-10}}{10^{-8} \times 10^{-8}} \text{ dynes} \approx 2.3 \times 10^{-3} \text{ dynes}$$

dynes being the unit of force in this system *viz.* the force which when acting on a mass of a gram causes an acceleration of 1 cm/s^2 as compared to the SI unit of force which is a Newton which is that force which acting on a mass of one kilogram would cause it to accelerate by a metre per second, implying that $1N = 1kg \; m/s^2 = 1 \times 10^3 g \times 10^2 \; cm/s^2 \approx 10^5$ dynes. Hence the force is what we got before as must be.

Thus we can see how much weaker are gravitational forces as compared to the electrostatic force. Yet we are always conscious of the pull of gravity and hardly aware of the eletrical. The reason is that gravitational forces are always attractive and hence all the matter of the earth exert a pull on us. On the other hand electrostatic forces can be attractive or repulsive depending on the signs of the charges being unlike or like respectively. Atoms and hence molecules (out of which we are made and also the earth) are composed of equal amounts of negative charges (due to the electrons) and positive charges (due to the nuclei) and are neutral and therefore the net Coulomb force is zero.

Returning to the Coulomb's Law for two particles with charges q and Q located at say $\vec{r}'$ and $\vec{r}$ respectively, the force on Q at $\vec{r}$ due to q at $\vec{r}'$ as given by eqn. (1*b*) may be written as

$$\vec{F} = \frac{1}{4\pi\epsilon_0} \frac{qQ(\vec{r} - \vec{r}')}{(|\vec{r} - \vec{r}'|)^3} \qquad \qquad ...(2)$$

as $\dfrac{\vec{r} - \vec{r}'}{|\vec{r} - \vec{r}'|}$ is the unit vactor along the line joining the two charges which we had previously called $\hat{r}$.

If there are several point charges located at $\vec{r}_1', \vec{r}_2', ..., \vec{r}_N'$ with charges $q_1, q_2, ..., q_N$ respectively, then the net force acting on the charge Q at $\vec{r}$ is the resultant or sum of these vectors yielding

$$\vec{F} = \frac{1}{4\pi\varepsilon_0} Q \sum_{i=1}^{N} q_i \frac{(\vec{r} - \vec{r}_i)}{|\vec{r} - \vec{r}_i|^3} \qquad \qquad ...(3)$$

It turns out to be not only convenient (but also a recognition of something tangible) to introduce the notion of the **electric field** $\vec{E}(\vec{r})$ at the point $\vec{r}$ through $\vec{F} = Q\vec{E}$ such that

$$\vec{E} = \frac{1}{4\pi\varepsilon_0} \sum_{i=1}^{N} q_i \frac{(\vec{r} - \vec{r}_i)}{|\vec{r} - \vec{r}_i|^3} \qquad \ldots(4)$$

and to say that this is the electric field at the point $\vec{r}$ due to charges $\{q_i\}$ placed at locations $\{\vec{r}_i\}$ $i = 1$, 2, ..., N, and to think of Q as a "test charge" which when placed at the point $\vec{r}$ would feel a force given by eqn. (2) due to the net electric field given by eqn. (3).

The notion of the field due to discrete point charges as defined above can be easily generalized to a continuous distribution of charge over a region with charge density distribution $\rho(\vec{r}')$.

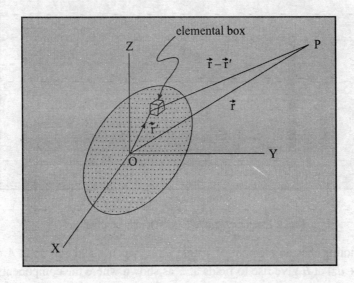

Fig. 1 The electric field at field point P due to a volume charge distribution

Suppose the charge density at the source point $\vec{r}'$ is $\rho(\vec{r}')$ then a small elemental box of volume $d^3\vec{r}' = dx'dy'dz'$ has net charge $\rho(\vec{r}')d^3\vec{r}'$ and this as can be seen from Fig. 1 is distant $|\vec{r} - \vec{r}'|$ from the

field point P. Thus the electric field at P due to this small infinitesimal box is $\dfrac{1}{4\pi\varepsilon_0} \dfrac{\rho(\vec{r}')d^3\vec{r}'}{|\vec{r} - \vec{r}'|^3}(\vec{r} - \vec{r}')$ by

Coulomb's Law and the definition of the field. The electric field due to the entire charge distribution is clearly given by simply integrating over the "shaded" region

$$\vec{E}(\vec{r}) = \frac{1}{4\pi\varepsilon_0} \int \frac{\rho(\vec{r}')d^3\vec{r}'(\vec{r} - \vec{r}')}{|\vec{r} - \vec{r}'|^3} \qquad \ldots(5)$$

In an analogous manner we may deal with the field due to a charge distribution along a line by introducing the linear distribution of charge λ per unit length, and that due to a charge distributed over a surface by defining the surface distribution of charge σ per unit area.

It is worthwhile at this point to consolidate our understanding of the Coulomb's Law and the notion of the Electric Field $\bar{E}$ through a few simple examples:

- Electric field due to a uniformly charged rod (λ units of charge per unit length) of length L at a point distant d lying on its perpendicular bisector.

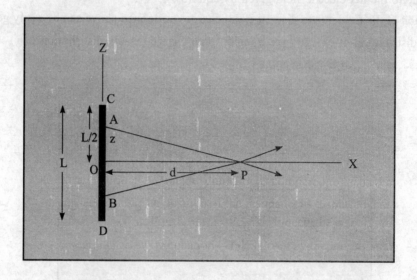

Fig. 2 Electric field due to a uniformly charged rod

We begin by noting that an element of lenght dz between z and $z + dz$ at A and a similar one between $-z$ and $-(z + dz)$ at B give rise to fields at P as shown where the components along the Z-axis cancel and ones along X add. The angle $\lfloor APO$ is $\tan^{-1}\dfrac{z}{d} = \cos^{-1}\left(\dfrac{d}{\sqrt{z^2+d^2}}\right)$.

Thus the X-component of the field at P is given by

$$E_x = \frac{1}{4\pi\varepsilon_0} \int_{-L/2}^{+L/2} \frac{\lambda dz}{z^2+d^2} \frac{d}{\sqrt{z^2+d^2}} = \frac{\lambda d}{4\pi\varepsilon_0}\left[\frac{1}{d^2}\frac{z}{(z^2+d^2)^{1/2}}\right]_{-L/2}^{+L/2}$$

as
$$\int \frac{dz}{(z^2+d^2)^{3/2}} = \frac{1}{d^2}\frac{z}{(z^2+d^2)^{1/2}} \quad \text{we have}$$

and

$$E_x = \frac{L\lambda}{4\pi\varepsilon_0 d\sqrt{d^2 + \dfrac{L^2}{4}}}.$$

In three-dimensions because of the cylindrical symmetry of the problem the electric field at the point P is best expressed in cylindrical coordinates

$$\vec{E} = \frac{L\lambda}{4\pi\epsilon_0\, d\sqrt{d^2 + \dfrac{L^2}{4}}}\hat{\rho}$$

where $\hat{\rho}$ is the unit vector pointing outwards and perpendicular to the rod, using the notation relevant to cylindrical coordinates. This $\hat{\rho}$ should not be confused with charge density.

As a check on the result as $L \to 0$ and $\lambda \to \infty$ such that $L\lambda \to Q$ we get $|\vec{E}| = \dfrac{Q}{4\pi\varepsilon_0 d^2}$ as should

be the case for a point charge and as $L \to \infty$ (infiniting long rod) we have $\dfrac{\lambda}{2\pi\varepsilon_0 d}\hat{\rho}$.

- Field due to a circular uniformly charged (λ per unit length) ring of radius R at an axial point at a distance d from the centre of the ring.

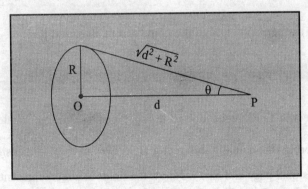

Fig. 3

Again from symmetry only the component of $\vec{E}$ along OP survives. All the points on the ring are at a distance $\sqrt{d^2 + R^2}$ from P. Hence all we have to do is to take the component along OP via.

$$\cos\theta = \frac{d}{\sqrt{d^2 + R^2}}$$

$$|\vec{E}| = \frac{1}{4\pi\varepsilon_0}\frac{(\lambda 2\pi R)}{(d^2 + R^2)}\frac{d}{\sqrt{d^2 + R^2}} = \frac{R\lambda d}{2\varepsilon_0(d^2 + R^2)^{3/2}}.$$

- Field due to a uniformly charged disc (σ units per unit area) of radius a at an axial point at a distance d from the centre of the disc.

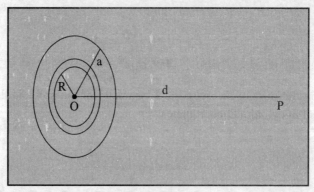

Fig. 4

Consider an annular ring with radii between R and $R + dR$. Its area is $2\pi R dR$ and hence it has a charge $2\pi R dR \sigma$ which replaces $\lambda 2\pi R$ of the previous problem and the electric field is again along OP and of magnitude

$$|\vec{E}| = \frac{1}{4\pi\varepsilon_0} \int_0^a \frac{2\pi R dR \sigma d}{(d^2 + R^2)^{3/2}} = \frac{2\pi\sigma d}{4\pi\varepsilon_0} \left(\frac{1}{d} - \frac{1}{\sqrt{a^2 + d^2}} \right)$$

Note that as $a \to \infty$ we have $|\vec{E}| \to \dfrac{\sigma}{2\varepsilon_0}$ which tells that the field due to an infinite plane sheet of

charge (σ per unit area) is perpendicular to the plane and of magnitude $\dfrac{\sigma}{2\varepsilon_0}$.

Section 2. ELECTRIC FIELD LINES AND GAUSS'S LAW

Let us examine the electric field vector due to a single positive charge located at a point. Because $\vec{E} = \dfrac{1}{4\pi\varepsilon_0} \dfrac{q\hat{r}}{r^2}$ remembering that actually this vector field lives in three-dimension, we depict it as we must on our two dimensional page and also we show the fields at a few representative points. Of course the vectors get smaller and smaller with r increasing since $|\vec{E}| \sim 1/r^2$ as we go further and further away and also bigger and bigger as we get closer to the point charge. Also this should look more like a hedgehog in three-dimensions. Faraday thought of a better way of depicting the field which is shown pictorically below, through **electric field lines**. Though at first sight it may appear that the electric field lines shown on the right hand side of Fig. 5 carry less information than the depiction of the magnitudes as well at each point of the field vector, this is not so. If we also assert that the density of field lines at each radial distance is proportional to the electric field, then in three dimensions since the surface area of a sphere is proportional to r^2, the number of field lines per unit area at a distance r from the point charge falls off as $1/r^2$ which is exactly how it should! However this is not true in two dimensions since the circumference of a circle is only proportional to r. But of course we are concerned with the world of three space dimensions in which we live. It is also instructive to look at field lines for an electric dipole viz. a positive and a negative charge (of equal and opposite strength) placed at a distance *a* apart.

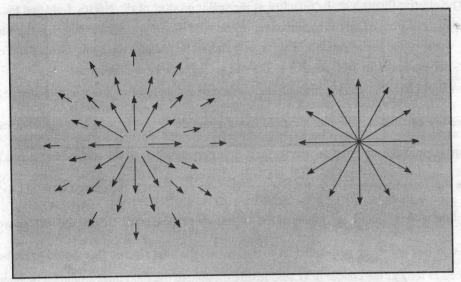

Fig. 5 $\bar{E}$ vectors due to a single charge and alongside we show field lines

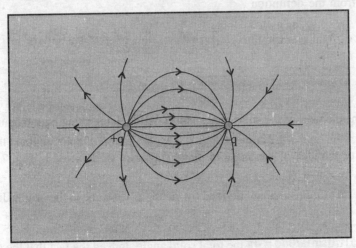

Fig. 6 Field lines due to an electric dipole of strength *qa*

From the example of the dipole it is clear that the tangent to the field line at any point gives the direction of the electric field there or in other words the force felt by a unit positive test charge place there. Note too that field lines begin at positive charges and terminate at negative charges or else they go off to infinite or from infinity terminate at negative charges.

In order to quantify the notion of 'density of field lines' we introduce the **electric flux** through any surface defined by the integral

$$\text{Electric Flux} = \int \vec{E} \cdot d\vec{S} \qquad \qquad ...(6)$$

where $d\vec{S}$ is the element of a surface (the normal to the surface gives the direction of this surface element). The electric flux is a scalar quantity as the scalar product of the electric field and the surface element vector is involved. Only the component of the field along $d\vec{S}$ contributes, viz. normal to the surface, by virtue of the scalar product. This is as it should be because the components parallel to the surface viz. perpendicular to $d\vec{S}$ (parallel to the surface) do not pierce the surface.

The total electric flux cutting through the surface of a sphere of radius r with a charge q at its centre is readily calculated. The electric field has magnitude $\dfrac{1}{4\pi\varepsilon_0}\dfrac{q}{r^2}$ which is constant over this spherical surface and at each point on the surface $\vec{E}$ is perpendicular to the surface and hence parallel to $d\vec{S}$, thus the Total Electric Flux $= 4\pi r^2 \times \dfrac{1}{4\pi\varepsilon_0} \times \dfrac{q}{r^2} = \dfrac{q}{\varepsilon_0}$. Even if the charge were not located at the centre of the sphere, though the values of the magnitude of the electric field at the surface would no longer be a constant nor $\vec{E}$ be perpendicular to the surface the total electric flux would again be $\dfrac{q}{\varepsilon_0}$ as before. Indeed as long as the charge is located **inside** the sphere the field lines would all be intercepted by it. It is also instructive to calculate the total flux due to a point charge at the centre of a sphere by directly integrating from the definition

$$\text{Total Electric Flux} = \int \vec{E} \cdot d\vec{S} = \frac{q}{4\pi\varepsilon_0} \int \frac{\hat{r}}{r^2} \cdot r^2 \sin\theta d\theta d\phi \hat{r}$$

$$= \frac{q}{4\pi\varepsilon_0} \int \sin\theta d\theta d\phi = \frac{q}{\varepsilon_0}$$

$\sin\theta d\theta d\phi \equiv d\Omega$ is the element of the solid angle as it is called. Integrating over θ from 0 to π and over ϕ from 0 to 2π we get the total solid angle which is 4π. The notion of solid angle is the generalization in three-dimensions of the idea of the angle in plane geometry as depicted in Fig. 7. The element of angle is the length of an infinitesimal arc divided by the radial distance to the origin. Just as $\displaystyle\int_0^{2\pi} d\theta = 2\pi$ we have $\displaystyle\int d\Omega = \int_0^{2\pi} d\phi \int_0^{\pi} d\theta \sin\theta d\theta d\phi = 4\pi$ the total solid angle. Indeed the fact that the total electric flux over a sphere for a charge q contained therein is $\dfrac{q}{\varepsilon_0}$ will be true for any closed surface enclosing the charge whatever be its shape as the total solid angle 4π would cancel the 4π in $\dfrac{1}{4\pi\varepsilon_0}$. In fact as Griffiths puts it so well "any old surface, whatever its shape, would trap the same number of field lines". Let us only add the adjective closed to the word surface. Charges outside the closed surface would not contribute as field lines enter and also leave in equal proportions. If there were more than one charge enclosed the total electric field would be the superposition of the contributions of each and

as a result the total electric flux would be $\dfrac{1}{\varepsilon_0}\Sigma q_i$. This result can also be, therefore, very simply

generalized to a continuum of charge with charge density $\rho(\bar{r})$ and thus we have

$$\oint_S \bar{E}\cdot d\bar{S} = \frac{1}{\varepsilon_0}\int_V p\,dV \qquad\qquad \text{...(7)}$$

where S is the closed surface enclosing the volume V. This is Gauss's Law for the Electric field in the Integral Form.

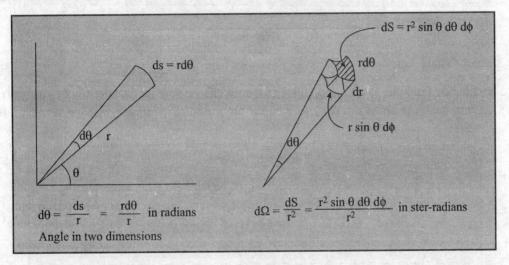

Fig. 7

If is worthwhile considering a few applications of Gauss's Law in determining electric fields due to various charge configurations:

- Electric field due to an infinitely long rod along the z-axis with charge density λ per unit length.

The problem has cylindrical symmetry about the z-axis. So we choose a Gaussian "pill-box" as shown in Fig. 8.

A cylinder of length z and radius ρ with the rod as its axis. The electric field (and field lines) by symmetry will be normal to the curved surface of the cylinder and parallel to the flat end surfaces. The magnitude of the electric field will be same on the surface of the cylinder and hence the total electric flux equals the area $2\pi\rho z$ of the curved surface into $\left|\bar{E}\right|$ which will be along $\hat{\rho}$ [The student should not confuse between ρ and $\hat{\rho}$ of the cylindrical coordinates with ρ which we have unfortunately also used for the charge density]. Thus $2\pi\rho z\left|\bar{E}\right| = \dfrac{1}{\varepsilon_0}z\lambda$.

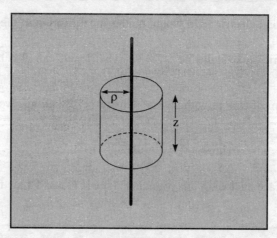

Fig. 8

Since the charge enclosed is clearly $z\lambda$. Thus we have $\vec{E} = \dfrac{\lambda}{2\pi\varepsilon_0\rho}\hat{\rho}$.

• Electric field due to an infinite plane sheet of charge with surface density of charge σ per unit area. The arrows in the figure below are meant to symbolise that we have an infinite sheet.

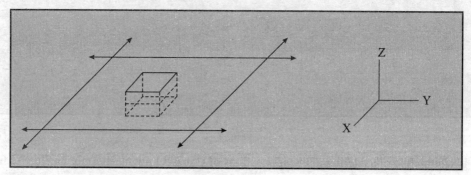

Fig. 9

Here from symmetry the electric field is at right angles to the plane (along the z-axis). We choose the Gaussian pill-box to have a cross-sectional area A extending a distance z above and z below the charged plane. The electric field above (from symmetry) points in a direction up and that below direction down and perpendicular to the charged plane. The sides of the pill-box being perpendicular to the electric field do not contribute to the electric flux and hence we have the total electric flux equal to $2\left|\vec{E}\right|A$ while the charge enclosed is $A\sigma$. Therefore from Gauss's Theorems $2\left|\vec{E}\right|A = \dfrac{1}{\varepsilon_0}A\sigma$

or
$$\vec{E} = \dfrac{\sigma}{2\varepsilon_0}\hat{k} \text{ above the plane}$$

$$= -\dfrac{\sigma}{2\varepsilon_0}\hat{k} \text{ below the plane}$$

$\hat{k}$ being the unit vector along the Z-axis.

● Electric field inside and outside an uniformly charged sphere of radius R (charge density ρ).

Here again because of symmetry we expect the electric field to be in the radial direction and hence we choose the Gaussian surfaces as concentric spheres of radius r with $r > R$ to get the field outside and $r < R$ to explore what it is inside. Thus we refer to Fig. 10.

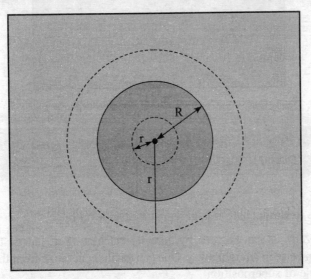

Fig. 10

At both the Gaussian surfaces shown by dashed lines the electric field is normal to the surfaces and of constant magnitude on all points on the surfaces.

Thus for $r > R$: We have total electric flux $= 4\pi r^2 \left| \vec{E} \right|$. The total charge enclosed is $\frac{4}{3}\pi R^3 \rho$

viz. the volume into the charge density. Thus by Gauss's Theorem $4\pi r^2 \left| \vec{E} \right| = \frac{1}{\varepsilon_0}\frac{4}{3}\pi R^3 \rho$ and hence we

have $\vec{E} = \frac{Q}{4\pi\varepsilon_0}\frac{1}{r^2}\hat{r} = \frac{\rho}{3\varepsilon_0}\frac{R^3}{r^2}\hat{r}$ the first step simply telling us that it is the same as that as if all the

charge were concentrated at the origin. [This is the same result as we had for the analogous gravitational interactions which enabled Newton to deal with the earth and the sun as point particles].

For $r < R$: Again the total electric flux is $4\pi r^2 \left| \vec{E} \right|$ as before but the total charge enclosed by the

Gaussian surface is now not the full charge but only a fraction $\frac{r^3}{R^3}$ of that.

Therefore, again by Gauss's Theorem we have $4\pi r^2 \left| \vec{E} \right| = \frac{1}{\varepsilon_0}\frac{4\pi}{3}r^3 \rho$ and hence we have $\vec{E} = \frac{\rho}{3\varepsilon_0}r\,\hat{r}$.

Note that at $r = R$ the expressions for the electric fields inside and outside match.

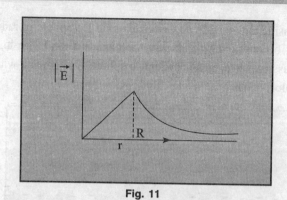

Fig. 11

Section 3. ELECTROSTATIC FIELD IS IRROTATIONAL AND CONCEPT OF SCALAR POTENTIAL

The electric field $\vec{E}$ due to **static** charges is given, at a basic level by $\vec{E} = \dfrac{1}{4\pi\varepsilon_0} \dfrac{q}{r^2} \hat{r}$. The curl of such an electrostatic field is zero, as can be seen by actually calculating it. Indeed there is nothing curly about a radial field as can be seen straight away. One can easily generalize from the field due to a single charge using the principle of superposition.

This property of the electrostatic field has a very important consequence. By virtue of the Stokes Theorem $\oint \vec{E} . d\vec{l} = \int (\vec{\nabla} \times \vec{E}) . d\vec{S}$. Since $\vec{\nabla} \times \vec{E} = 0$, therefore $\oint \vec{E} . d\vec{l} = 0$. This implies that the integral of $\vec{E} . d\vec{l}$ from any point $\vec{a}$ to a point $\vec{b}$ is independent of the path. This enables us to define a function $\phi(\vec{r})$ known as the potential at $\vec{r}$ through the integral.

$$\phi(\vec{r}) = -\int_{\vec{r}_0}^{\vec{r}} \vec{E} . d\vec{l} \qquad \qquad ...(8)$$

where $\vec{r}_0$ is an arbitrarily chosen convenient reference point. As observed in Chapter 5 on Vector Analysis (Section 4) a curl-less field is the a gradient of a scalar field.

Thus we may write

$$\vec{E} = -\vec{\nabla} \phi(\vec{r}) \qquad \qquad ...(9)$$

The potential $\phi(\vec{r})$ due to a point charge of magnitude q located at the origin is

$$\phi(\vec{r}) = -\int_{\infty}^{\vec{r}} \frac{q}{4\pi\varepsilon_0 r^2} \hat{r} . d\vec{l} = -\int_{\infty}^{r} \frac{q}{4\pi\varepsilon_0} \frac{dr}{r^2} = \frac{q}{4\pi\varepsilon_0 r} \qquad \qquad ...(10)$$

We have chosen the reference point to be infinity. One can see that $Q\phi(\vec{r})$ is physically the work done to bring a charge Q from infinity to the point $\vec{r}$. It is also evident that the potential also obeys the superposition principle. The unit of potential in the S.I. system is Joules per Coulomb which is called a volt.

Again it is profitable to illustrate the basic ideas through an example:

- What is the electrostatic potential both inside and outside due to a charge Q distributed uniformly over a spherical shell of radius R?

Because of the spherical symmetry of the problem choose Gaussian surfaces as spheres of radius r that arc concentric with the spherical shell (radius R) of charge. $\vec{E}$ must be radial by symmetry

$r > R$: Total electric flux $= (4\pi r^2) \left| \vec{E} \right| = \dfrac{1}{\varepsilon} Q$

$$\vec{E} = \frac{Q}{4\pi\varepsilon} \frac{1}{r^2} \hat{r}$$

$r < R$: $\vec{E} = 0$ (as there is no charge enclosed within that Gaussian surface).

$\therefore$ Potential ϕ at a point $\vec{r}$ out side the charged spherical shell is $\phi(\vec{r}) = -\displaystyle\int_{\vec{r}_0}^{\vec{r}} \vec{E} . d\vec{l}$

$= -\displaystyle\int_{\infty}^{r} \frac{Q}{4\pi\varepsilon} \frac{1}{r^2} dr$ wherein the last step we have chosen the reference point r_0 to be infinity. Thus

$$\phi(r) = \frac{Q}{4\pi\varepsilon} \frac{1}{r} \text{ for } r > R$$

For $r < R$ as $\vec{E} = 0$ because there is no enclosed charge we must have $\phi = $ constant

Also ϕ must be continuous at $r = R$ and thus we have

$$\phi(r) = \frac{Q}{4\pi\varepsilon} . \frac{1}{r} \text{ for } r > R$$

$$= \frac{Q}{4\pi\varepsilon} \frac{1}{R} \text{ for } r \le R$$

Section 4. GAUSS'S LAWS IN DIFFERENTIAL FORM, THE POISSON AND LAPLACE EQUATIONS

The Gauss's Law as we have discussed so far, namely for any closed surface the total electric flux

$$\oint_S \vec{E} \cdot d\vec{S} = \frac{1}{\varepsilon_0} Q$$

where Q is the total charge enclosed by the surface.

This law is in the form of an integral equation.

However this can be converted to its differential form through the use of the Divergence Theorem due to Gauss [see Chapter 5 eqn.(5)], namely

$$\oint_S \vec{v} \cdot d\vec{S} = \int_V \vec{\nabla} \cdot \vec{v} dV$$

where $\vec{v}$ is any vector field, S a closed surface, V the volume contained by it. Thus the left hand side of the Gauss's Law may through the use of this theorem be written as

$$\oint_S \vec{E} \cdot d\vec{S} = \int_V \vec{\nabla} \cdot \vec{E} dV$$

On the other hand the left hand side using Gauss's Law may be written as

$$\oint \vec{E} \cdot d\vec{S} = \frac{1}{\varepsilon_0} Q = \frac{1}{\varepsilon_0} \int_V \rho(\vec{r}) dV$$

as the volume integral of the charge density ρ over the enclosed volume is the total charge enclosed,

Therefore $\int_V \vec{\nabla} \cdot \vec{E} dV = \frac{1}{\varepsilon_0} \int_V \rho(\vec{r}) dV$ and since this holds for any volume, the two integrands must

be equal and hence $\vec{\nabla} \cdot \vec{E} = \frac{1}{\varepsilon_0} \rho$ ...(11)

This is the Gauss's Law expressed in differential form.

We have already seen in the previous section that $\vec{E}$ can be expressed as the gradient of a scalar function $\vec{E} = -\vec{\nabla}\phi$ where ϕ is the electrostatic potential. Inserting this in eqn.(11) we arrive at the equation

$$\nabla^2 \phi = -\rho/\varepsilon_0$$ ...(12)

this partial differential equation is known as the Poisson equation.

In the regions where there are no charges ($\rho = 0$) we have

$$\nabla^2 \phi = 0$$ ...(13)

which is the Laplace's equation.

While finding the electric fields due to a given charges directly using the Coulomb's Law and the definition of the field in terms of the force involved doing some sums or integrals over the distribution of charges, the Gauss's Law in the integral form was very efficacious provided there was underlying symmetry in the charge distribution. In the absence of such symmetry the problem is in general more difficult. However the Laplace and Poisson equations while involving the solution of partial differential equations are for a scalar function, the potential ϕ, which is a simpler object and the electric fields may

be obtained at various points in space through the gradient operation $\vec{E} = -\vec{\nabla}\phi = -\hat{i}\frac{\partial}{\partial x}\phi - \hat{j}\frac{\partial}{\partial y}\phi - \hat{k}\frac{\partial}{\partial z}\phi$.

□□□

7 Current Electricity and Magnetic Effect of Steady Currents

Section 1. CONDUCTORS AND CURRENTS

For the study of the physics of currents (or charges in motion) two important developments were necessary. The first was the invention of the voltaic cell and its improvements which provided (through the use of the chemistry of ionic compounds in solution) a source of electromotive force (emf) such that a constant electrical potential difference could be maintained between its two terminals. The second was the fact that metals could be drawn into wires through which constant currents could be made to flow. The later important fact found was actually an empirical "law" (an observed property of conductors at a fixed temperature) known as Ohm's Law. The total current (I) flowing through a given wire from one electrode to another (anode to cathode is the convention), is proportional to the potential difference V across the conductor

$$I = \frac{1}{R} V \qquad \qquad ...(1)$$

where R is called the resistance. The resistance would of course depend on the specifics of the wire (linearly proportional to its length L and inversely on the cross-sectional area A) and so one defines $\left(R = \rho \frac{L}{A} \right)$ the resistivity ρ which is the property of the material out of which the wire is made and the inverse of the resistivity is known as the conductivity $\sigma = 1/\rho$.

If we define $\vec{j}$ as the electric current density, then $I = \int \vec{j} \cdot d\vec{S}$ integrated over the cross-section of the wire is the current. On the other hand the potential difference across the ends of the conducting wire is $V = -\int \vec{E} \cdot d\vec{l}$. Treating $\vec{j}$ and $\vec{E}$ as constant vectors along the length and cross-section of the wire $I = |\vec{j}| A$ and $V = |\vec{E}| L$, we have, since $I = \frac{1}{R} V \Rightarrow |\vec{j}| A = \frac{1}{R} |\vec{E}| L \Rightarrow |\vec{j}| = \frac{L}{AR} |\vec{E}|$,

$$\vec{j} = \sigma \vec{E} \qquad \qquad ...(2)$$

which may be called the differential form of the Ohm's Law. Here σ is supply a material property. Of course there are semiconductors, super-conductors and what not but for our present purposes we shall ignore these as simply variants of the basics which helped Ampere and others to study the fundamental physics of electric and magnetic fields.

Let us tentatively choose the Ampere (A) as the unit of current defining it for the time being as a Coulomb (C) per second. Remember always that the choice of which units are fundamental and which are derived is a very practical matter. Is it good to define the Ampere as a Coulomb per second or is it that we should define a Coulomb as the charge that a current of one Ampere carries in one second? We agree on what can be measured more accurately and hence we shall come back to this question when this whole edifice is in place. Thus with I in Amperes and V in volts (= Joules/Coulomb) the resistance

R is expressed in Ohms (often abbreviated as Ω or volts per ampere). The unit of resistivity $\rho = \dfrac{RA}{L}$ is clearly ohm-metre. The reciprocal of resistance (called conductance) is measured in 1/Ohm also called mho which is ohm read backwards in Urdu style. In modern usage a mho is called a Siemens. So the unit of conductivity is siemens per metre.

Before discussing in a heuristic manner the mechanism of conduction let us discuss the notion of the electromotive force or emf. In the words of E.M. Purcell emf is "any influence that causes charge to circulate around a closed path". The energy required to do so could come from a chemical process such as what goes on in a cell or a battery of cells, or could also be of electromagnetic origin (as we shall see in the next chapter) or a thermocouple working on temperature differences, etc. The electromotive force is defined through

$$\text{emf} = \in \ = \oint \vec{E} \cdot d\vec{l} \qquad \qquad ...(3)$$

Of course this closed line integral would have been zero for an electrostatic $\vec{E}$ but now the situation is different. The name used for this quantity is a misnomer because $\in$ is **not** a force. It is dimension-wise work done per unit charge.

Unlike the situation in electrolytic conduction (the basic laws of which were given by Faraday) where the ionic compound NaCl when dissolved in water partially dissociates in the positive Na^+ and the negative Cl^- ions which carry the current to the cathode and the anode respectively, in metallic conduction the electrons are responsible for the flow of the current. Because the convention of what is a positive charge and what is negative was already fixed from the good old days of static electricity the electrons according to that convention were determined to possess, on their discovery, a negative charge. The conventional direction of the current from the anode to the cathode in the circuit to which the terminals of the cell were connected was deemed to be positive which is opposite to the direction of flow of the actual charge carried by the electrons. This however is merely a matter of convention and need not concern us henceforth.

In a metal such as copper there is one electron per atom (in its outermost shell) which is bound the least and when all these atoms come together to form the copper metal in bulk, these electrons get delocalized, that is they can wander around in the metal with the residual Cu^+ ions providing a background of positive charge. The ions when in a crystal form a lattice and is at stable equilibrium but you do have oscillations about the equilibrium positions that increase as one increases the temperature.

At first sight it would appear that these loosely bound electrons, one from each copper atom, now in the metal belonging to the bulk body and not to individual atoms should behave like free electrons, should respond to the electric field and through their movement constitute the electric current. If this were so then each electron with charge e and mass m would suffer an acceleration of magnitude a in the direction of the externally applied electric field $\vec{E}$ given by the Newton's equation of motion

$$ma = eE$$

and hence after a time t the velocity of each electron would be

$$\frac{eE}{m}t$$

Therefore the current which should be the number of carriers times the velocity, times e the charge of each, would be expected to increase with time. However this is totally wrong because experiment tells us that we have a **steady** current and **not** one that increases with time.

The solution to this puzzle is that the electrons are not really free. Their motion through the wire is not ballistic (determined by the external electric field alone). They collide with the ions and these collisions with the randomly moving ions (under thermal agitation) serve to randomize the motion of the electrons, but for the steady applied electric field. The inelastic collisions of the electrons with ions serve to provide a frictional force $-\gamma\vec{v}$ proportional to the velocity of the electron and that quickly the electrons achieve a drift velocity where the force due to the electric field $\vec{E}$ balances the frictional force, much as the raindrop falling under gravity and impeded by the frictional force offered by the air achieves a terminal or drift velocity. Thus we expect that we have

$$e\vec{E} = \gamma\vec{v}_D \qquad \qquad ...(4)$$

The drift velocity $\vec{v}_D$ now being proportional to $\vec{E}$ the basis of the Ohm's Law now becomes plausible. Of course the detailed understanding requires the use of Quantum Mechanics which governs the physics at the level of atoms.

This broad physical picture is also in accord with the fact that resistance increases with temperature as the randomising role of the lattice to the motion of electrons increases as the vibrational motion of the lattice increases with increasing temperature.

Section 2. CONSERVATION OF CHARGE AND THE EQUATION OF CONTINUITY

From the study of a huge variety of processes involving atoms, nuclei and elementary particles one finds that before and after reactions, and decay processes the total electric charge remains unchanged. This is known as a global conservation law because it does not refer to a locality in space. But actually more is true, in the sense that we have a local conservation of charge as well.

This local conservation of charge is expressed through an equation of continuity as it is called. We have already seen that the divergence of a vector (as an example we read in Chapter V Section 2 the example of a vector field describing the velocity field of a fluid) is a measure of the fluid leaving a region (if $\vec{\nabla}\cdot\vec{v}$ is positive). If we take the charge current density $\vec{j}$ and we find a positive value, of $\vec{\nabla}\cdot\vec{j}$ then some charge is surely leaving that region and hence the charge density ρ must be getting smaller there

$$\frac{\partial\rho}{\partial t} = -\vec{\nabla}\cdot\vec{j} \qquad \qquad ...(5)$$

This is known as the equation of charge continuity.

Equivalently one could arrive at the same result by writing down an expression for the charge inside a volume V in terms of the charge density

$$Q(t) = \int_V \rho(\vec{r},t)\,dV \qquad \ldots(6)$$

The charge flowing out through the closed surface S bounding that region is given by

$$\int_S \vec{j}(\vec{r},t)\cdot d\vec{S} \qquad \ldots(7)$$

Local conservation of charge would dictate that for any such volume enclosed by a surface

$$\frac{dQ}{dt} = -\int_S \vec{j}\cdot d\vec{S} \qquad \ldots(8)$$

But using equation (6), we have

$$\frac{dQ}{dt} = \int_V \frac{\partial \rho}{\partial t}(\vec{r},t)\,dV \qquad \ldots(9)$$

Thus

$$\int_V \frac{\partial \rho}{\partial t}\,dV = -\int \vec{j}\cdot d\vec{S} \qquad \ldots(10)$$

But by the divergence theorem of Gauss

$$\oint_S \vec{j}\cdot d\vec{S} = \oint_V \vec{\nabla}\cdot\vec{j}\,dV \qquad \ldots(11)$$

and therefore vide equation (11) and equation (10), we have

$$\int \frac{\partial \rho}{\partial t}\,dV = -\int \vec{\nabla}\cdot\vec{j}\,dV$$

But since this is true for any such enclosed volume V we must have the continuity equation [eqn. (5)].

We shall see later that the Maxwell's equations after the introduction by him of the so-called displacement current has the equation of continuity as a natural consequence.

Section 3. THE MAGNETIC FIELD AND THE MAGNETIC MOMENT

Certain special materials (known as ferromagnets) such as Fe_3O_4 which occurs naturally in an ore called lodestone and other materials such as steel are capable of being brought into a condition when they are said to be magnetized. If such a sample is suspended such that it is free to rotate about a vertical axis it aligns itself in a particular direction which happens to be close to the geographic north-south direction at any place on earth. Similarly a magnetic needle made of steel pivoted in its centre in such a manner that it is free to rotate in the horizontal plane, it comes to rest aligning itself along the "magnetic meridian" or line of "magnetic longitude". In a like-wise manner a magnetic needle pivoted in such a way as to be free to rotate in a vertical plane (an instrument known as the dip-circle) aligns itself to the horizontal making an angle equal to the "magnetic lattitude" of a given spot on earth. Thus, it is the contention of the present author, that if not explicitly, in an implicit manner from very practical considerations the explorers and navigators in the age of geographical discovery were studying the "earth's magnetic field", unconsciously no doubt, using the magnetic needle (the compass and the dip circle) as detectors.

In hindsight we may try to understand this tendency of the magnetic needle to align itself along the magnetic field by using an analogy of an electric dipole (a positive charge q and a negative charge $-q$ fixed at a distance a from each other) in a uniform electric field $\vec{E}$.

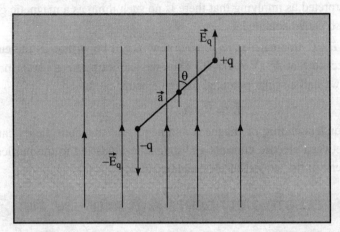

Fig. 1 An electric dipole in uniform electric field $\vec{E}$

As can be seen from the figure there is no net force on this dipole. However there is a torque $\vec{\tau} = q\vec{E} \times \vec{a} = \vec{E} \times \vec{d}$ where in the last step we have defined $q\vec{a} \equiv \vec{d}$ the electric dipole moment. Note that the magnitude of the torque is given by

$$|\vec{\tau}| = |\vec{E}||\vec{d}|\sin\theta$$

where θ is the angle between the dipole moment and the electric field. Equilibrium will result if the torque is zero *viz.* $\theta = 0$. Thus the electric dipole will tend to align itself along the electric field. This is minimum energy configuration. Indeed the energy of an electric dipole $\vec{d}$ in a uniform electric field $\vec{E}$ is $-\vec{E} \cdot \vec{d}$.

We could try to understand the reason for a magnetic needle to align with the magnetic field by an analogous argument by saying that the magnet is a "magnetic dipole" having a magnetic moment $\vec{\mu}$ and that the magnetic field $\vec{B}$ exerts a torque on it

$$\vec{\tau} = \vec{B} \times \vec{\mu} \qquad \qquad ...(12)$$

and that the energy of the magnetic moment in a uniform magnetic field is $-\vec{\mu} \cdot \vec{B}$ and that it comes to equilibrium by aligning itself along $\vec{B}$.

Up to the point that we may think in terms of magnetic moments or even 'dipoles' the argument is basically correct. Where it goes wrong is that there are no magnetic monopoles. A magnet cut into two gives us two magnets and so on. And indeed unlike electric field lines magnetic field lines have no beginning or end which is another way of saying the same thing, (the lines that go out come back again) and this would imply that

$$\vec{\nabla} \cdot \vec{B} = 0 \qquad ...(13)$$

or in view of the divergence theorem $(\oint \vec{B} \cdot d\vec{S} = \int \vec{\nabla} \cdot \vec{B} dV)$ we have the total magnetic flux through a closed surface is zero.

$$\oint \vec{B} \cdot d\vec{S} = 0 \qquad ...(14a)$$

which can also be interpreted as implying that there is no such thing as a magnetic charge. Fields with zero divergence are also called solenoidal.

Indeed since $\vec{\nabla} \cdot \vec{B} = 0$ this enables us to state that $\vec{B}$ can be written as the curl of a vector *viz.* $\vec{\nabla} \times \vec{A}$. It is easily checked that $\vec{\nabla} \cdot (\vec{\nabla} \times \vec{A}) = 0$. Thus we can introduce a vector potential $\vec{A}$ for the magnetic field just as we had a scalar potential for the electric field:

$$\vec{B} = \vec{\nabla} \times \vec{A} \qquad ...(14b)$$

But the correct understanding of magnetic moments and magnetic fields came only after the intimate connection between electric currents and magnetic fields led to the unification of electrical and magnetic phenomena in the subject of electromagnetism.

Section 4. STEADY ELECTRIC CURRENTS AND MAGNETIC FIELDS

Before 1820 there was no known link between electrical and magnetic phenomena except for some mathematical similarities. It was Oersted's discovery of the magnetic interaction (with a compass needle) of steady electric currents and also that exerted by a magnet brought close to current carrying wire that the connection between these two seemingly different types of forces was uncovered. Ampere studied these phenomena quantitatively and helped provide the underlying mathematical formalism. He also provided the equation expressing the magnetic interaction between currents. Indeed he even anticipated to some extent our present understanding that at the basic level magnetism arises from currents in the atomic scale (now we know that this is due to electrons orbiting around nuclei and electrons spinning so to say about their axes).

In order to develop the basics of the interaction involving steady electric currents and magnetic field we shall first discuss the Biot-Savart Law which gives us the magnetic field produced by a steady electric current. Next we go on to find the force due to a magnetic field on a current element. We then consider the magnetic force between two current carrying wires, mainly because this is useful in defining the ampere in the S.I. units. Then we move on to a more basic level the Lorentz force due to a uniform magnetic field on a uniformly moving point charge. We close the chapter with the essence of the magnetic affects of currents through the Ampere's law in both integral and differential forms.

The Biot-Savart Law gives us the magnetic field $\vec{B}$ at some point P due to a circuit carrying a current I. Let $\vec{dl}$ be an element of length along the wire at some point as shown in the figure.

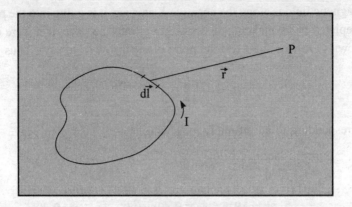

Fig. 2

The magnetic field at P due to the current carrying wire will be given by

$$\vec{B} = \frac{\mu_0}{4\pi} I \oint \frac{d\vec{l} \times \hat{r}}{r^2} \qquad \text{...(15)}$$

where the constant $\mu_0 = 4\pi \times 10^{-7} \, \text{N/A}^2$ known as the permeability of free space in SI units. In the integral over the closed circuit l along the wire and r are measured in metres. The magnetic field is measured in N/A.m which is known as tesla (T).

In the Gaussian cgs system the unit of the magnetic field is quite appropriately called the gauss. 1 tesla $=10^4$ gauss. For orientation the earth magnetic field is approximately half a gauss.

As before to consolidate our ideas about the Biot-Savart Law we consider a few concrete examples:

• Find the magnetic field $\vec{B}$ at a point distant s from a straight wire (of length long enough compared to s so that it may be considered to be infinitely long) carrying an electric current I.

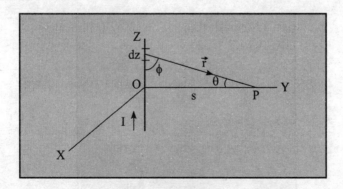

Fig. 3

Here $d\vec{z} \times \vec{r} = -(dz)\sin\phi \hat{i}$ as magnitude of the vector product is the product of the lengths into the sine of the angle between them. So, as $\sin\phi = \cos\theta$ (see Fig. 3) we have

$$d\vec{z} \times \vec{r} = -dz\cos\theta \hat{i}$$

Thus $\vec{B}$ the magnetic field is along the negative *X*-axis *viz.* it is going into the page perpendicular to it. This is often depicted by $\otimes$ meaning an arrow going into the page, if it were coming out of the page it would be shown $\odot$ as (the shaft and the point of the arrow so to say). Thus

$$\vec{B} = -\hat{i}\frac{\mu_0}{4\pi}I\int_{-\pi/2}^{+\pi/2}\frac{dz\cos\theta}{r^2}$$

taking the limits corresponding to an infinitely long wire.

Now $\qquad\qquad r = \dfrac{s}{\cos\theta}$ and $z = s\tan\theta$

or $\qquad dz = s\sec^2\theta\, d\theta \Rightarrow \dfrac{dz\cos\theta}{r^2} = s\dfrac{\sec^2\theta\, d\theta\cos^2\theta}{s^2}\cos\theta = \dfrac{\cos\theta\, d\theta}{s}$

Thus, $\qquad\qquad \vec{B} = -\dfrac{\mu_0 I}{4\pi s}\hat{i}\int_{-\pi/2}^{+\pi/2}\cos\theta\, d\theta$

Thus, $\qquad\qquad \vec{B} = \dfrac{(-\hat{i})(4\pi\times10^{-7}\,T.m/A)\times(I.A)}{4\pi s}$

Hence we have

$$\vec{B} = -\hat{i}\frac{I}{s}10^{-7}\,T$$

where the magnetic field is in tesla, the current *I* should be expressed in amperes, the distance *s* in metres.

• Magnetic field due to a circular loop of radius *R* carrying a current *I* at a distance *s* above its centre

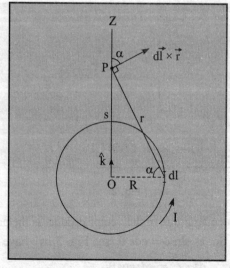

Fig. 4

For ease of visualization take an element of current $d\vec{l}$ at a point shown in the plane of the circle carring the current perpendicular to the plane of the paper. This $d\vec{l}$ is a vector going perpendicularly into the paper. $\hat{r}$ is a vector in the plane of the paper. Therefore $d\vec{l} \times \hat{r}$ is in the plane of the paper at right angles to $\hat{r}$ as shown. As we move the element around the circle the vector $d\vec{l} \times \hat{r}$ and hence $d\vec{B}$ traces out a cone. The only component that will survive the integration over the loop will be that along OP. Thus calling OP the Z-direction and the unit vector along it to be $\hat{k}$ we have (putting in $\cos\alpha$ to project the surviving component)

$$\vec{B} = \hat{k}\frac{\mu_0 I}{4\pi}\oint\frac{\cos\alpha dl}{r^2} = \hat{k}\frac{\mu_0 I}{4\pi}\frac{2\pi R}{r^2}\cdot\frac{R}{r}$$

as

$$\oint dl = 2\pi R \text{ and } \cos\alpha = R/r \cdot \text{Since } r^2 = R^2 + s^2$$

$$\vec{B} = \frac{\mu_0 I R^2}{2(R^2 + s^2)^2}\hat{k} \qquad \text{...(16)}$$

The force exerted by a magnetic field on a current carrying loop is given by

$$\vec{F} = I\oint d\vec{l} \times \vec{B} \qquad \text{...(17)}$$

• Again let us illustrate through an example: What is the force on a long straight wire (1m long) due to a uniform magnetic field $\vec{B}$ which is at right angles to the wire?

$$\vec{F} = I\oint d\vec{l} \times \vec{B} = I(\oint d\vec{l}) \times \vec{B} \qquad \text{(isolating the line integral)}$$

which we can do if $\vec{B}$ is uniform. We assumed that the wire is long enough to assume that end effects are unimportant. Since the wire and the field are perpendicular to each other the force is of magnitude.

$$|\vec{F}| = BIl$$

where l is the length of the wire. Here B is in tesla, I is amperes and l in metres.

Combining equation (15) for the magnetic field due to a current carrying loop and equation (17) for the force exerted by a magnetic field on a current carrying loop we can find the force exerted by one current carrying loop (labelled 1) on another such loop (labelled 2) with currents I_1 and I_2 flowing through them respectively

$$\vec{F}_{12} = \frac{\mu_0}{4\pi}I_1 I_2 \oint_1 \oint_2 d\vec{l}_2 \times \frac{d\vec{l}_1 \times \hat{r}}{r^2} \qquad \text{...(18)}$$

This relation is important for defining the unit of current - the ampere - in the SI system.

The magnetic field due to a current (I_1) carrying infinite wire at a distance s from it is given (as we have seen) by

$$B = \frac{\mu_0}{2\pi}\frac{I_1}{s} \qquad \text{...[following eqn. (15)]}$$

and the force exerted by this magnetic field on another such wire (current I_2) placed as distance s from the field producing wire and placed parallel to it would be $|\vec{F}| = BI_2 l$ as $\vec{B}$ and the direction of the wire are perpendicular to each other.

Thus, the force per unit length between two infinitely long straight wires parallel to each other at distance s, would be attractive in nature and of magnitude

$$\frac{F}{l} = \frac{\mu_0}{2\pi} \frac{I_1 I_2}{s} \qquad \qquad ...(19)$$

This is used for the definition of the ampere in the SI system.

The ampere is the current which when flowing in each of two infinite parallel wires (of negligible cross-section, separated by a distance of one metre, would result in a force per unit length between the wires of $2 \times 10^{-7}\,\text{N/m}$.

The coulomb in this system of units is defined as the charge transported in one second by a current of one ampere.

The Lorentz force

From our discussion of the force exerted by a magnetic field on a current carrying loop described by equation (17) *viz.* $\vec{F} = I \oint d\vec{l} \times \vec{B}$, one may be tempted to write for a straight stretch L that the force is

$I\vec{L} \times \vec{B} = \frac{q}{T}\vec{L} \times \vec{B}$ where we have suggested that $I = \frac{q}{T}$ *viz.* charge flowing past per unit time and to

write $\frac{\vec{L}}{T} = \vec{v}$ the velocity of the particle carrying the charge, and hence it would appear the $\vec{F} = q\vec{v} \times \vec{B}$.

This led Lorentz to suggest that just as a stationary charge q in an electric field $\vec{E}$ experiences a force $q\vec{E}$, if the charge were moving in a magnetic field $\vec{B}$ with velocity $\vec{v}$ it would feel a force $q\vec{v} \times \vec{B}$ putting both these together we have the so-called **Lorentz force** for a particle of charge q moving in an electric **and** a magnetic field

$$\vec{F} = q\vec{E} + q\vec{v} \times \vec{B} \qquad \qquad ...(20)$$

Once again to familiarize ourselves with the underlying notions of the Lorentz force we consider a few examples and applications:

• Show that a particle of charge q moving with a velocity $\vec{v}$ in a uniform magnetic field does not do any work and that its orbit is a circle, a helix or a straight line depending on the initial conditions.

The force $q\vec{v} \times \vec{B}$ is perpendicular to $\vec{v}$ and since $\vec{v} \cdot \vec{F} = q\vec{v} \cdot (\vec{v} \times \vec{B})$ is the rate of doing work which is zero, therefore no work is done whatsoever. Thus from the conservation of energy the kinetic energy of the particle and hence its speed (magnitude of the velocity) has to remain unaltered. If the initial velocity is such that it is perpendicular to $\vec{B}$ than the orbit is a circle with the centripetal acceleration provided by the $q\vec{v} \times \vec{B}$ of magnitude qvB:

$$\frac{mv^2}{r} = qvB \Rightarrow r = \frac{mv}{qB}$$

If initial $\vec{v}$ is along $\vec{B}$ there is no force acting on the particle and the trajectory is a straight line. If the initial $\vec{v}$ makes an angle θ with $\vec{B}$ the particle has a circular motion in the plane perpendicular to $\vec{B}$ super imposed on a linear motion along $\vec{v}$ giving a trajectory which is a spiral (helix).

Ampere's law

We have seen by applying the Biot-Savart Law to obtain the magnetic field due to an infinite straight wire carrying a current I that

$$|\vec{B}| = \frac{\mu_0 I}{2\pi s}$$

at a distance s from the wire.

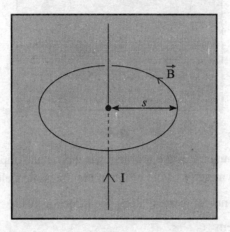

Fig. 5

If you close the fist of your right hand with the thumb pointing up the direction of your fingers trace the magnetic field lines.

If we now perform the line integral of $\vec{B} \cdot d\vec{l}$ around a circular path of radius s centred on the wire then we have

$$\oint \vec{B} \cdot d\vec{l} = \oint \frac{\mu_0 I}{2\pi s} dl = \frac{\mu_0 I}{2\pi s} \oint dl = \mu_0 I$$

as $\oint dl = 2\pi s$. We note that the result is **independent** of the choice of s. Actually the result is even more general. Any loop provided it **encloses** the current carrying wire actually yields the same result and if it **does not** enclose any current carrying element the result of the integral in zero.

If instead of a single current carrying wire we have a bunch of current carrying wires by the fact that the magnetic fields would simply superpose we shall get $\mu_0 I$ where I is the sum of the currents in the individual wires. Even if we had a continuum - a volume current density $\vec{j}$ then the current through the surface enclosed by the closed loop of integration would contribute and we would have

$$\oint \vec{B} \cdot d\vec{l} = \mu_0 \int \vec{j} \cdot d\vec{S} \qquad \qquad \text{...(21)}$$

This is the Integral Form of Ampere's Law.

Again we consolidate our understanding with a few examples of the application of Ampere's Law:

• Magnetic field due to an infinite straight wire carrying a current I at a distance s.

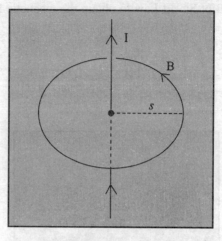

Fig. 6

Noting the cylindrical symmetry of the problem we choose an Amperian circuit or loop which is a circle of radius s. From the symmetry of the problem the magnetic field $\vec{B}$ must be circumferential (with no radial component and no component along the direction of the wire). Thus $\oint \vec{B}.d\vec{l} = 2\pi s |\vec{B}|$

Thus by Ampere's Theorem

$$2\pi S |\vec{B}| = \mu_0 I \Rightarrow |\vec{B}| = \frac{\mu_0 I}{2\pi s}$$

in agreement with our previous result using the Biot-Savart Law.

• Magnetic field due to a uniformly distributed current flowing through an infinitely long cylindrical rod of radius a.

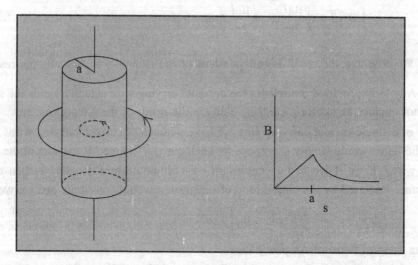

Fig. 7

Again we exploit the cylindrical symmetry to choose two typical Amperian circuits or loops as circles of radius s one inside the cylinder and one outside centred on the axis as shown in the figure.

$s < a$
$$\oint \vec{B} \cdot d\vec{l} = 2\pi s |\vec{B}|$$

$$\mu_0 \oint \vec{j} \cdot d\vec{S} = \mu_0 J \frac{s^2}{a^2}$$

the part of the total current J enclosed by the Amperian circle inside is $J \dfrac{\pi s^2}{\pi a^2}$ as it is proportional to the area through which the current is flowing.

Thus inside the cylinder

$$|\vec{B}| = \frac{\mu_0}{2\pi} \frac{J}{a^2} s$$

$s > a$
$$\mu_0 \oint \vec{J} \cdot d\vec{S} = \mu_0 J$$

are thus outside the cylinder
$$|\vec{B}| = \frac{\mu_0}{2\pi} \frac{J}{s}$$

giving the magnitude of $|\vec{B}|$ as a function of s as shown in the figure.

• Magnetic field due to an infinite solenoid having a radius a and n turns per unit length carrying a current I.

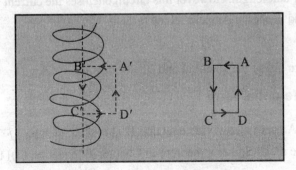

Fig. 8

The solenoid carrying the current I has been shown with spacings exaggerated for clarity. We mean to have closely wounded coils so that we have cylindered symmetry about the axis. Since we also have translational symmetry parallel to the axis we shall exploit that to choose Amperian loops so that we can find the magnetic field both inside and outside the solenoid. The typical Amperian loop ABCD, a rectangle of unit length and some width AB = CD is shown alongside the solenoid in the figure. From symmetry we expect $\vec{B}$ to be parallel to the axis of the solenoid.

Taking this loop completely outside the solenoid we notice that $\int \vec{B} \cdot d\vec{l}$ along AB and CD must be zero as the magnetic field everywhere along these sides is perpendicular to the displacement.

The values of $\int \vec{B} \cdot d\vec{l}$ along BC and DA must be equal and opposite because the loop encloses no current viz. $\oint \vec{B} \cdot d\vec{l} = 0$.

This can only happen if $|\vec{B}|$ is independent of the distance from axis of the solenoid. But infinitely far from the axis of the cylinder we expect $|\vec{B}| \to 0$ and therefore $|\vec{B}|$ must be zero everywhere outside the solenoid !

Next let us take this rectangular loop ABCD completely inside the solenoid. Again because from symmetry the magnetic field here too must be along the axis of the solenoid, $\int \vec{B} \cdot d\vec{l}$ is zero along AB and along CD. Since the loop totally inside does not enclose any current whatsoever the integral from B to C and from D to A must cancel each other. This implies that the magnitude of the magnetic field $|\vec{B}|$ must be the same along these two lines. Hence the magnetic field inside must be a constant.

Lastly take out rectangular Amperian loop to a place where B'C' lies inside the solenoid and A'D' lies outside. We show this in the figure explicitly through the amperian loop in dotted lines. Again A'B' and C'D' are paths along which $\int \vec{B} \cdot d\vec{l}$ gets no contribution. The same is true about path D'A' simply because $\vec{B} = 0$ outside the solenoid. Thus the only non-vanishing contribution is from B'C' which is $|\vec{B}| \times 1$ because B'C' is of unit length. However this circuit encloses the current running through n turns of the solenoid viz. nI and hence by Ampere's Law

$$|\vec{B}| = \mu_0 nI$$

along the axis everywhere inside the solenoid and $\vec{B} = 0$ outside.

Ampere's law in differential form

The integral form of the Ampere's Law vide equation (21) is $\oint \vec{B} \cdot d\vec{l} = \mu_0 \int \vec{j} \cdot d\vec{S}$ as we have already seen and applied. Now we recall Stokes's theorem in Chapter V [equation (7)] that for any vector field $\vec{v}$ we have

$$\oint \vec{v} \cdot d\vec{l} = \int (\vec{\nabla} \times \vec{v}) \cdot d\vec{S}$$

or the line integral of a vector field $\vec{v}$ taken over a closed curve C is equal to the surface integral of the curl of $\vec{v}$ taken over a surface having C as a boundary. Therefore, $\int \vec{B} \cdot d\vec{l} = \int (\vec{\nabla} \times \vec{B}) \cdot d\vec{S}$ and accordingly the Ampere's Law in its integral form may be re-written as

$$\int (\vec{\nabla} \times \vec{B}) \cdot d\vec{S} = \mu_0 \int \vec{j} \cdot d\vec{S}$$

Now this must be true for any such surface S and bounding curve C, and therefore we must have

$$\vec{\nabla} \times \vec{B} = \mu_0 \vec{j} \qquad \qquad ...(22)$$

This is the differential form of the Ampere's Law.

We shall see later that this equation will need to be amended in time dependent situations.

In conclusion to this chapter we note in summary that while in electrostatics we had

• the Coulomb Law written let us say in the form given by equation (22) of Chapter 6.

$$\vec{F} = q\vec{E} = \frac{q}{4\pi\varepsilon_0} \int \frac{\rho(\vec{r}')}{|\vec{r} - \vec{r}'|^3} d^3\vec{r}'(\vec{r} - \vec{r}')$$

• the Gauss's Law given by equation (22) of that chapter

$$\oint \vec{E} \cdot d\vec{S} = \frac{1}{\varepsilon_0} \int_V \rho dV$$

In this chapter on magnetic fields due to steady currents we had

• the basic Biot-Savart's Law [given by equation (15)]

$$\vec{B} = \frac{\mu_0}{4\pi} I \oint \frac{d\vec{l} \times \hat{r}}{r^2}$$

and

• the Ampere's Law given by equation (21)

$$\oint \vec{B} \cdot d\vec{l} = \mu_0 \int \vec{j} \cdot d\vec{S}$$

While the Coulomb Law in electrostatics and the Biot-Savart's Law in magnetism due to currents gives us the basic detailed relationship between the fields $\vec{E}$ and $\vec{B}$ and the sources (charge density and current), the Gauss's Law in the former case and the Ampere's Law in the latter have a more global connotation or implication.

Indeed one may with justification say that what the Gauss's Law is to the Coulomb Law in electrostatics, the Ampere's Law is to the Biot-Savart Law with regard to the magnetic effects of steady currents. As we have seen through a few examples if there is some basic symmetry in the nature of the sources (charges and currents) then Gauss's Law in electrostatics and Ampere's Law in the context of magnetic effects of steady currents provide the most efficient way of determining the resulting fields. However, if there is a situation where such symmetrics are not available then we have to fall back on the more painstaking calculations using the Coulomb's Law in the electrostatic case and the Biot-Savart's Law for magnetic fields due to steady currents. Indeed most practical situations fall under this category.

□□□

8   Electromagnetic Induction and the Maxwell's Equations

So far we have been concerned with Electrostatics and Steady Currents and Magnetic Fields, we have not discussed time dependence.

In 1831 Michael Faraday from a series of experiments made the fundamental discovery that when the magnetic flux threaded by a closed conducting loop is changed then a current flows through the wire, viz. an electromotive force is induced, and that the induced emf(ϵ) is proportional to the rate of change of the magnetic flux ($\Phi \equiv \oint \vec{B} \cdot d\vec{S}$) enclosed by the closed loop.

$$\epsilon = \oint \vec{E} \cdot d\vec{l} = -\frac{d\Phi}{dt} \qquad \qquad \ldots(1)$$

The significance of the negative sign was emphasised by Lenz: The direction of the induced emf is so directed that it opposes the very cause that generates it.

To clarify this statement : suppose the magnetic flux increases then the emf generated will be such that the current flowing through the loop will be in such a direction that the change in the magnetic field due to the current induced will be such as to tend to decrease the flux.

This statement sometimes called Lenz's Law expresses in the context of electromagnetic induction a more general principle due to Le Chatelier that any system has the tendency to counter-act changes in its state. One may call it inertia!

The unit of magnetic flux is the weber (wb). If the rate of variation of the magnetic flux is 1 wb/s then the emf induced in the loop is 1 V (volt). Note that flux in SI units is tesla metre squared (Tm^2) which is the weber, while flux in the Gaussian cgs unit is gauss centimetre squared thus the ratio of the SI unit of flux to the gaussian cgs unit of flux is 10^8 as 1 m = 10^2 cm and 1 Tesla is 10^4 gauss.

We discuss a few examples of applications of Faraday's Law of Electromagnetic induction:

• Current induced by change in magnetic flux through a conducting loop near a current carrying straight wire. The magnetic flux threading the conducting loop may be changed with time in various ways as shown in the accompanying figure. By bringing the loop closer or further from the magnetic field producing linear current or by moving the current carrying wire towards or away from the loop. By changing the current in the current carrying wire. The curved arrows marked emf shown the direction of the induced emf in each case. The symbol ⊗ B means the magnetic field due to the current carrying wire is perpendicular to the page and going into it.

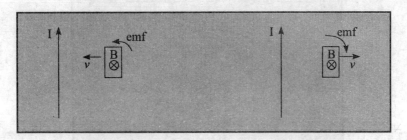

Fig. 1

• Conducting wires separated by a distance L apart and connected to a resistance as shown in the accompanying figure has the current completed through a movable connecting link.

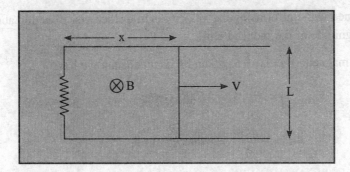

Fig. 2

This system is in a uniform magnetic field B going into and perpendicular to the page. If the sliding wire is pulled in such a manner that it moves with a uniform velocity V as shown in the diagram, what should be the current flowing through the circuit?

The magnetic flux through the closed circuit is

$$\Phi = LxB$$

and thus the induced emf is

$$\epsilon = -\frac{d\Phi}{dt} = -BLv$$

as $\dfrac{dx}{dt} = v$. Therefore the current through the circuit given by Ohm's Law is

$$IR = \epsilon \Rightarrow I = \frac{\epsilon}{R} = \frac{BLv}{R}$$

The direction of the current through the circuit is clockwise in accordance with Lenz's Law.

- A circular loop of radius R with N turns of wire in a plane perpendicular to the plane of the page is placed in a uniform constant magnetic field $\vec{B}$ as shown figure.

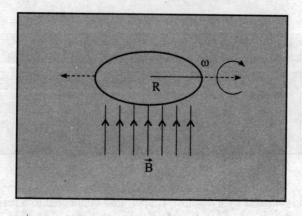

Fig. 3

If now the coil is turned with uniform angular velocity ω in a clockwise direction about the dotted line what will be the magnitude of the induced emf?

Since the total magnetic flux is $\oint \vec{B} \cdot d\vec{S}$ and $\vec{B}$ is a constant we have

$$\oint = N\vec{B} \cdot \vec{A} = NB\pi R^2 \cos \omega t$$

Thus,

$$|\in| = \left| -\frac{d\Phi}{dt} \right| = NB\omega\pi R^2 \sin \omega t,$$

a source of alternating voltage. The sense of the current induced is left to the student to determine using Lenz's Law.

Section 2. FARADAY'S LAW OF INDUCTION IN DIFFERENTIAL FORM

From the integral form of Faraday's Law of electromagnetic induction given by equation (1), viz.

$$\in = \oint \vec{E} \cdot d\vec{l} = -\frac{d}{dt}\Phi$$

and noting that Φ the total magnetic flux is given by

$$\Phi = \int \vec{B} \cdot d\vec{S}$$

over the surface with the closed circuit constituting the bounding curve, we have

$$\oint_C \vec{E} \cdot d\vec{l} = -\frac{d}{dt}\int_S \vec{B} \cdot d\vec{S}$$

...(2)

Now let us apply Stokes's Theorem [equation (7) in Section 3 of Chapter V] to convert the line integral on the left hand side into a surface integral

$$\oint \vec{E} \cdot d\vec{l} = \int (\vec{\nabla} \times \vec{E}) \cdot d\vec{S} \qquad \text{...(3)}$$

Using this result we can rewrite equation (2) as

$$\int_S (\vec{\nabla} \times \vec{E}) \cdot d\vec{S} = -\frac{d}{dt} \int_S \vec{B} \cdot d\vec{S} \qquad \text{...(4)}$$

Since this equation must be true for any surface enclosed by any closed loop, the only way this can be ensured is that the integrand of the surface integral agree on both sides and thus

$$\vec{\nabla} \times \vec{E} = -\frac{\partial}{\partial t} \vec{B} \qquad \text{...(5)}$$

we have changed the total derivation to a partial derivative since $\vec{B}$ in general could also dependent on space (which of course goes out in the surface integral).

It may be noted that in a time independent scenario $\frac{\partial \vec{B}}{\partial t} = 0$ and accordingly equation (5) reduces to $\vec{\nabla} \times \vec{E} = 0$. Indeed this was the situation in electrostatics and the fact that $\vec{E}$ is irrotational (that is its curl in static situation is zero) enabled us to write $\vec{E} = -\vec{\nabla}\phi$ as the curl of a gradient is zero.

Another implication of equation (5) is that a time varying magnetic field gives rise to an electric field. Again we have this intimate relationship between electricity and magnetism. Just as magnetism arises not only from magnetic materials (lodestone etc.) but also from electric currents (via Oersted and Ampere) electric fields do not only owe their origin only to charges but also to time varying magnetic fields.

Section 3. MAXWELL'S DISPLACEMENT CURRENT

The essence of what was known about electromagnetism at the time of Maxwell written down in our modern compact notation was contained in the following four equations

(a) $\vec{\nabla} \cdot \vec{E} = \frac{1}{\varepsilon_0} \rho$ (Gauss's Law)

(b) $\vec{\nabla} \cdot \vec{B} = 0$ (absence of magnetic monopoles)

(c) $\vec{\nabla} \times \vec{B} = \mu_0 \vec{j}$ (Ampere's Law)

(d) $\vec{\nabla} \times \vec{E} = -\frac{\partial \vec{B}}{\partial t}$ (Faraday's Law of Induction)

Maxwell noted a serious difficulty with equation (c) the Ampere's Law. The experimental basis of the Ampere's Law was through the study of magnetic fields due to **steady** currents. We have a contradiction when we try to apply this to non-stationary situations *viz.* to time dependent phenomena.

Consider the act of charging or discharging of a condensor.

When we switch on the key of the circuit the condensor is charged and after it is charged we may switch off the key and disconnect the battery. Now if once again we switch on the key the charged condenser begins to discharge and most definitely the plates of the capacitor acts as sinks or sources of charge respectively in the two cases; and indeed a transient current does flow through the circuit in both the cases of charging and discharging shown in Fig. 4.

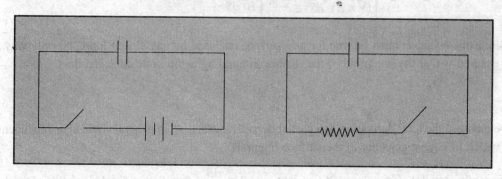

Fig. 4

However, if we take the divergence of the equation (c) above (at the start of this section) representing Ampere's Law we obtain $\vec{\nabla} \cdot (\vec{\nabla} \times \vec{B}) = \mu_0 \vec{\nabla} \cdot \vec{j}$. But since the divergence of the curl of a vector field is zero (see Chapter V) this leads to the erroneous result that

$$\vec{\nabla} \cdot \vec{j} = 0 \qquad \qquad ...(6a)$$

erroneous, because from the physical meaning of the divergence [see Chapter V, Sector 2] it is a measure of the sources and/or sinks. Indeed the equation of continuity expressing the conservation of electric charge [see Section 2 of the present chapter] we must have [vide equation (5)]

$$\vec{\nabla} \cdot \vec{j} = -\frac{\partial \rho}{\partial t} \qquad \qquad ...(6b)$$

Now using the Gauss's Law $\vec{\nabla} \cdot \vec{E} = \frac{1}{\varepsilon_0} \rho$ we may rewrite the equation of continuity as

$$\vec{\nabla} \cdot \left(\vec{j} + \varepsilon_0 \frac{\partial \vec{E}}{\partial t} \right) = 0$$

So Maxwell asserted that to accomodate time dependent situations the Ampere's Law must be amended by adding to the conduction current density $\vec{j}$ an additional 'displacement current' $\varepsilon_0 \frac{\partial \vec{E}}{\partial t}$ and accordingly we should write

$$\vec{\nabla} \times \vec{B} = \mu_0 \left(\vec{j} + \varepsilon_0 \frac{\partial \vec{E}}{\partial t} \right) \qquad \qquad ...(7)$$

The physical meaning of the displacement current is best illustrated by the example of the charging of a parallel plate condensor with plate area A and distance a between them. If the current in the circuit is say I then the rate of increase of charge density on the plates per unit times is I/A. But the electric field between such parallel plates is $|\vec{E}| = \dfrac{\sigma}{\varepsilon_0}$ (where σ is the surface charge density - see Fig. 9 in

Chapter V). Thus the magnitude of the displacement current density is $\varepsilon_0 \dfrac{\partial |\vec{E}|}{\partial t} = \varepsilon_0 \dfrac{1}{\varepsilon_0} \dfrac{d\sigma}{dt} = \dfrac{I}{A}$ and

hence the displacement current is $\dfrac{I}{A} \times A = I$, assuring us that the total displacement current between

the plates equals the conduction current in the wire and the current is continuous as it should be.

.   The introduction of the displacement current by Maxwell was an extremely important step indeed as while for slowly time varying fields the magnetic field due to the conduction current is overwhelmingly large compared to that due to the displacement current, for rapidly varying fields the displacement current could be dominant and indeed as we shall see in the next section this is what makes possible electromagnetic waves.

Section 4. MAXWELL'S EQUATIONS AND THE ELECTROMAGNETIC WAVE

With the inclusion of the displacement current the full-blown Maxwell's equations read

$$\vec{\nabla} \cdot \vec{E} = \frac{1}{\varepsilon_0} \rho \qquad \qquad ...(8a)$$

$$\vec{\nabla} \cdot \vec{B} = 0 \qquad \qquad ...(8b)$$

$$\vec{\nabla} \times \vec{E} = -\frac{\partial \vec{B}}{\partial t} \qquad \qquad ...(8c)$$

$$\vec{\nabla} \times \vec{B} = \mu_0 \vec{j} + \mu_0 \varepsilon_0 \frac{\partial \vec{E}}{\partial t} \qquad \qquad ...(8d)$$

To these we may append the Lorentz force law for the action of electric and magnetic fields on a charged particle (charge q) and velocity $\vec{v}$

$$\vec{F} = q(\vec{E} + \vec{v} \times \vec{B}) \qquad \qquad ...(9)$$

The equation of continuity follows by simply taking the divergence of Ampere's Law with Maxwell's amendment and the fact that $\vec{\nabla} \cdot (\vec{\nabla} \times \vec{B}) = 0$ and use of Gauss's Law. Equations (8) and equation (9) constitute the basis of our understanding of **all** phenomena associated with electricity and magnetism.

We now analyse equations (8) to look at electric and magnetic fields in a vacuum that is a region where there are no charges and currents $(viz. \rho = 0 = \vec{j})$

The Maxwell's equations in vacuum are thus

$$\vec{\nabla} \cdot \vec{E} = 0 \qquad \qquad ...(10a)$$

$$\vec{\nabla} \cdot \vec{B} = 0 \qquad \qquad ...(10b)$$

$$\vec{\nabla} \times \vec{E} = -\frac{\partial \vec{B}}{\partial t} \qquad \qquad ...(10c)$$

$$\vec{\nabla} \times \vec{B} = \mu_0 \varepsilon_0 \frac{\partial \vec{E}}{\partial t} \qquad \qquad ...(10d)$$

These are a set of four coupled first order linear homogenous differential equations for $\vec{E}$ and $\vec{B}$.

The first step towards simplification is to decouple the equations for $\vec{E}$ and $\vec{B}$. This is done by taking the curl of equations (10c) and (10d) and using (10d) and (10c) respectively to acheive this purpose

$$\vec{\nabla} \times (\vec{\nabla} \times \vec{E}) = -\vec{\nabla} \times \frac{\partial}{\partial t} \vec{B} = -\frac{\partial}{\partial t} \vec{\nabla} \times \vec{B} = -\mu_0 \varepsilon_0 \frac{\partial^2 \vec{E}}{\partial t^2} \qquad ...(11)$$

where in the last step we have used equation (10d). Also similarly

$$\vec{\nabla} \times (\vec{\nabla} \times \vec{B}) = \mu_0 \varepsilon_0 \vec{\nabla} \times \frac{\partial \vec{E}}{\partial t} = \mu_0 \varepsilon_0 \frac{\partial}{\partial t} \vec{\nabla} \times \vec{E} = -\mu_0 \varepsilon_0 \frac{\partial^2 \vec{B}}{\partial t^2} \qquad ...(12)$$

where is the last step we have used equation (10c). Note that in achieving this de-coupling between and $\vec{E}$ and $\vec{B}$ fields the cost that we paid was to now having to deal with second order differential equations in space and time, but as we shall see that this is worth the price!

With the curl of the curl of the electric and magnetic fields on the left hand sides of equations (11) and (12) we invoke a vector identity true for any vector fields $\vec{F}$ namely

$$\vec{\nabla} \times (\vec{\nabla} \times \vec{F}) = \vec{\nabla}(\vec{\nabla} \cdot \vec{F}) - \nabla^2 \vec{F} \qquad \qquad ...(13)$$

Working out this identity is straightforward since we know how to take a curl of a vector field and we know the meanings of the gradient, divergence and Laplacian from our discussion on Vector Analyses in Chapter V. However it is tedious, so that if you work it out once in your lifetime you can store the result in your memorable achievements.

Implementing the identity [equation (13)] on the left hand side of equation (11), we have

$$\vec{\nabla} \times (\vec{\nabla} \times \vec{E}) = \vec{\nabla}(\vec{\nabla} \cdot \vec{E}) - \nabla^2 \vec{E} = -\nabla^2 \vec{E} \qquad \qquad ...(14)$$

where in the last step we put $\vec{\nabla} \cdot \vec{E} = 0$ using equation (10a). Giving a similar treatment to equation (12), we have

$$\vec{\nabla} \times (\vec{\nabla} \times \vec{B}) = \vec{\nabla}(\vec{\nabla} \cdot \vec{B}) - \nabla^2 \vec{B} = -\nabla^2 \vec{B} \qquad \qquad ...(15)$$

where in the last step we put $\vec{\nabla} \cdot \vec{B} = 0$ using equation (10b).

Thus through the step of decoupling the equations by taking the curl and using vector identities we have arrived at two equations for the electric and magnetic fields in vacuum

$$\nabla^2 \vec{E} = \mu_0 \varepsilon_0 \frac{\partial^2 \vec{E}}{\partial t^2} \qquad \qquad ...(16a)$$

$$\nabla^2 \vec{B} = \mu_0 \varepsilon_0 \frac{\partial^2 \vec{B}}{\partial t^2} \qquad \qquad ...(16b)$$

Comparing these with equation (6) of Section 2 in Chapter 4 on waves in Module two on Vibration and Waves we see that once more we have a wave equation except for two important aspects: firstly in

place of $\dfrac{\partial^2}{\partial x^2}$ we now have $\nabla^2 = \dfrac{\partial^2}{\partial x^2} + \dfrac{\partial^2}{\partial y^2} + \dfrac{\partial^2}{\partial z^2}$ namely a wave equation in three dimensions; and secondly, in place of a scalar amplitude we now have the wave equation for vector fields $\vec{E}$ and $\vec{B}$.

Note that the velocity of the wave is

$$c = \frac{1}{\sqrt{\varepsilon_0 \mu_0}} .$$ ...(17)

Putting is numbers for ε_0 and μ_0 we see that the velocity of this wave is 3×10^8 m/s which happens to be the velocity of light. From Coulomb's Law and the Biot-Savart Law experimental observations on charges and currents one had the values of ε_0 and μ_0 and Lo and Behold! one has, coming out of it all, waves with velocity equal to that of light!

Section 5. MONOCHROMATIC PLANE WAVE SOLUTIONS OF MAXWELL'S EQUATIONS

Let us consider a plane wave. This means that the wave front is a plane. Let us choose this plane to be parallel to the XY plane so that the wave varies only along the Z-direction. Thus the electric and magnetic fields vary only along the Z-direction and with time. Accordingly we see for solutions to the wave equations (16a) and (16b) of the form

$$\vec{E} = \vec{E}_0 e^{i(kz - \omega t)}$$ ...(18a)

$$\vec{B} = \vec{B}_0 e^{i(kz - \omega t)}$$ ...(18b)

when $\vec{E}_0$ and $\vec{B}_0$ are complex constant vectors. Of course our physical $\vec{E}$ and $\vec{B}$ will be the real parts of $\vec{E}$ and $\vec{B}$. As we have seen earlier the use of complex variables simplifies the algebra. We immediately notice that as t increases the point of constant phases corresponds to z increasing. This means that the wave propagates along the z-direction moving rightwards (increasing z). Also at a given time the field

repeat their values as z increases by $\dfrac{2\pi}{k}$. This then is the wavelength $\lambda = \dfrac{2\pi}{k}$ and k is the wave-number. Similarly at a given point in space the fields get repeated after a time $\dfrac{2\pi}{\omega} \equiv T$, the periodic time and

thus $\dfrac{1}{T} = \dfrac{\omega}{2\pi} \equiv v$ is the frequency and ω the angular frequency. The velocity of the wave is given by

$kz - \omega t =$ constant, which tells us that $\dfrac{dz}{dt} = \dfrac{\omega}{k}$. Substituting (18a) and (18b) in the wave equations

(16a) and (16b) we get $k^2 = \mu_0 \varepsilon_0 \omega^2$ or $\omega / k = \dfrac{1}{\sqrt{\varepsilon_0 \mu_0}} = c$ the velocity of light [vide equation (17)].

Thus we have a plane wave travelling in the z-direction with a velocity $C = \dfrac{1}{\sqrt{\varepsilon_0 \mu_0}}$ with a frequency $\nu = \dfrac{\omega}{2\pi}$ and a wavelength $\lambda = \dfrac{2\pi}{k} = \dfrac{c}{\nu}$.

This is a monochromatic plane wave.

Now the fact that $\vec{\nabla} \cdot \vec{E} = 0 \Rightarrow (E_0)_z k = 0 \Rightarrow (\vec{E}_0)_z = 0$ which means that the electric field is in the XY plane and similarly $\vec{\nabla} \cdot \vec{B} = 0$ inform us that $(\vec{B}_0)_z = 0$ and hence the electric and magnetic fields lie in a plane perpendicular to the direction of propagation (here taken to be along z).

Lastly using Faraday's Law of Induction $\vec{\nabla} \times \vec{E} = -\dfrac{\partial \vec{B}}{\partial t}$ we obtain $i\vec{k} \times \vec{E}_0 = +i\omega \vec{B}_0$ where $\vec{k} = (0,0,k)$ since we have taken the wave to move along the z-axis. Thus we have $\vec{E}$, $\vec{B}$ and $\vec{k}$ at right angles to each other and we can express our result through a schematic figure shown below:

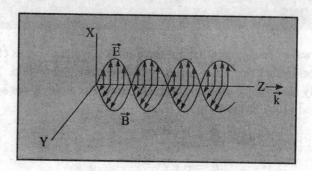

Fig. 5

Thus Fig. 5 represents a transverse electromagnetic wave travelling along the Z direction with a wave vector $\vec{k} = (0, 0, k)$ and wavelength $\lambda = \dfrac{2\pi}{k}$ moving with velocity c. It is polarised with the electric field along the X-direction and the magnetic field along the Y-direction.

This prediction of Maxwell that it is possible to have electromagnetic waves was experimentally verified by Hertz who showed that an oscillating charge which he created through electrical sparks between two electrodes gave rise to electromagnetic waves of wavelength more than of the order of centimetres which we now call Hertzian or radio waves. Subsequently electromagnetic waves of shorter wavelengths (of the order of millimetres and centimetres) were found by our own Jagadish Chandra Bose and are known as microwaves. And it was realized that infrared and visible radiation too belong to this family of electromagnetic waves, as also do the still shorter wavelength ultraviolet and X-rays down to gamma radiation emitted by nuclei. All these waves travel in vacuum with a velocity of $\sim 3 \times 10^8$ m/s.

□□□